GW00374812

Long, Short and Tall: stories and poems from our lives

Michael Hermann
and
David Blake

with contributions by
Susan Hermann, Peter Hermann
and Paul Palmer

3P
PUBLISHING

Text Copyright © Michael Hermann, David Blake, Susan Hermann, Peter Hermann and Paul Palmer, 2020

All rights reserved

No part of this publication may be lent, resold, hired out or reproduced in any form or by any means without written permission from the authors and publisher.
All rights reserved.

Copyright © 3P Publishing
CEC, London Road
Corby
NN17 5EU

A catalogue number for this book is available from the British Library

ISBN: 978-1-913740-06-1

Cover design: James Mossop

Contents

The Authors   1
Introduction   3
School   5
On Starting School *Michael Hermann*   6
First Class *David Blake*   9
School Play *David Blake*   10
School Targets *David Blake*   14
On Becoming a Grammar Grub *Michael Hermann*   16
Going to Big School *Peter Hermann*   24
Early Days   33
The Winter of 1947 *David Blake*   34
Codin's Cap *David Blake*   37
If Music Be the Food of Love *Peter Hermann*   44
Family   52
Youngest in the Family *David Blake*   53
The Visit *David Blake*   56
Sir Percy Blake *David Blake*   58
Telephone Calls to a Relative Stranger *Su Hermann*   62
Memories   71
Childhood Street *Paul Palmer*   72
Day Trips *David Blake*   78
Cut the Crap *Michael Hermann*   81
Places   86
Delapre Abbey *David Blake*   87
London *Michael Hermann*   93
Activities and Pastimes   95
Right Place – Wrong Time *David Blake*   96
Marathon? What Marathon? *Michael Hermann*   101
Jubilee Gardens *Michael Hermann*   103
Like Rabbits Caught in the Glare *David Blake*   104
Water-Skiing at Grendon Lakes *Michael Hermann*   106

Difficult Times 112

Cobweb *Michael Hermann* 113

Tourbillon *Michael Hermann* 114

Uninhabitable *Michael Hermann* 115

Hide and Seek *Michael Hermann* 116

The Three Peaks Challenge *Michael Hermann* 117

Jobs and Careers 118

Moving On *Su Hermann* 119

On Becoming an Academic *Michael Hermann* 127

You Look Wonderful Tonight *Michael Hermann* 135

And to Close... 145

Acknowledgements 146

The Authors

Thank you to the following authors who have given their permission for their written work and photographs to be included in this book.

Michael Hermann: Born in Brixworth and now living in Rutland, Michael trained as an accountant before entering higher education as a lecturer in accounting and finance. He was encouraged by his wife and close friends to research and write his family history, 'Eighty Years On', which was published in November 2019. Michael's experiences of academia and life in general are reflected in his stories and poems in this volume.

David Blake: A former primary school teacher and education adviser, David was inspired by his father remarking that "a pun is the lowest form of bread." Many of his pieces began as oral stories, told at Feast of Fools, Northampton's storytelling club, and Babble of Naseby, a spoken word group. He has run the Northampton Hope Centre creative writing group for seven years. Like Michael, he is a season ticket holder at Northampton Town Football Club.

Susan Hermann: Originally from Shropshire, Su has lived in many locations in England, but in Northamptonshire and Rutland in more recent years. She enjoyed a diverse and interesting career which included working at Fylingdales, British Airways, the probation service, but predominantly in the banking industry. She enjoys walking, photography and travelling around Europe - when permitted!

Peter Hermann: Born in Brixworth, Peter now lives in West Sussex where he enjoys playing tennis, walking, cycling and painting in oils. Peter spent many years teaching junior aged children and his stories are drawn from his own personal experience of the learning process and life at 'The Big School'. They highlight the frustration, fear, ridicule, guilt and sense of failure he experienced as he interacted with the teaching and education process during the early 1960s.

Paul Palmer: Born and educated in Market Harborough, Paul presently lives on the border of Rutland in the village of Medbourne. Following a career in furniture restoration, Paul spends his days walking and enjoying numerous crafts. In his youth Paul had the wanderlust; he hitch-hiked to Morocco and together with his wife, Carol, worked in Canada. They also travelled to Eastern Turkey in a Morris Traveller, camping out for six months. Their next trip is on the Silk Road through Uzbekistan in April 2021. Paul enjoys writing observational poetry and performing - in a club in Market Harborough and also for friends.

Introduction
Michael Hermann and David Blake

Given the 'lock-down' period necessary because of Covid-19, and other extremely important factors, the years 2019 and 2020 have been challenging ones for the authors featured in this book. However, the enforced lack of normality in daily life has also provided an opportunity for reflection and the possibility of being gainfully employed in a creative project. The authors and their wives, Su and Gail, agreed that no better opportunity was likely to arise for us all to collaborate on this project.

Michael published his own book, 'Eighty Years On', in 2019, a comprehensively researched volume about his family history. However, over the years he had written about many other subjects, in several different forms, and these have been revisited and extended for this book.

Also in 2019, David co-ordinated the publication of 'Writing in Hope', a book of creative writing by clients of Northampton Hope Centre, a local charity supporting disadvantaged people. He has written a collection of poems and stories, mainly about growing up in the 1950s as part of a large family.

The decision was made to collate some of this material and to invite Susan Hermann and two others to contribute to this publication. One of these was Michael's brother, Peter, and the other was Paul Palmer, a friend of Michael and Su. Four of the contributors are in their seventies, the other approaching it at speed! As a matter of fact, Michael and David were born within two weeks and 200 yards of each other. .

Most of the entries are autobiographical but there are also fictional stories, some definitely heading for the "tall" description contained in the title. All the contributors have their individual style and memories but given the era in which they grew up, there are some common themes, ones which will be recognised by readers of a certain age and, hopefully, by readers of an uncertain age as well.

Please be aware that it has been necessary to sometimes disguise the name of a person within contributions. One author, in particular, sincerely hopes that one character will never read this book, or if he or she does, that they will not recognise themselves!

During the period of lock-down / social distancing, the five contributors have ploughed on with their contributions in splendid isolation. In terms of compiling the materials or having discussions between the contributors, there was never any mention of using 'Zoom', 'Skype', 'Facetime,' or indeed anything similar that might otherwise have caused some of the contributors to suffer irreversible writer's block! Instead, we have managed the convenient technology of e-mail communication and computer file handling in order to prepare this book for publication.

We hope you enjoy reading it!

School

Brixworth Primary School

On Starting School
Michael Hermann

Other contributors to this book describe a number of fascinating aspects of their education. My own thoughts and memories may mirror some of their own reminiscences but, hopefully, will add some different insights of my own.

My earliest memory of my primary school at Brixworth, Northamptonshire was not a pleasant one. Five years old and seated in my desk in the schoolroom situated opposite the Buttercross in the older part of the village, I recall being mortified by the sight of a very large house spider which resided in one of the school cupboards. I was so disturbed that Mrs Battison, the teacher, had to remove the insect from my sight.

I recall the standard reading books of those early days, with large print and accompanying pictures; I found these quite easy to read and I must have progressed well in this respect. One day Mrs Battison asked the class what day it was. "Wednesday," we all shouted. "And who can spell Wednesday?" she challenged. I was invited to reply and got it right! I wouldn't be so confident today!

Generally my academic progress during my first five years of education was very good, but my time at Brixworth School was not all success and I managed to make a fool of myself from time to time. For example, my explanation to Mrs Moody's class in Year Three that thunder was 'caused by God moving the furniture around' caused great amusement for everyone in the group, except, of course, for me. I blame my father for that explanation, but it did demonstrate a certain gullibility in my character.

Whilst I generally warmed to the more gentle, quietly spoken teachers, I feared the ones who would shout at us in anger and frustration. Mrs Moody was one who, I thought, had an appropriate name, but the Head teacher, Mr Hopkins, scared me dreadfully, especially in his sessions devoted to arts and crafts activities at which I was particularly useless. He also had a large cane which he used frequently but, fortunately, never on me.

I tended to be accident prone in those early days. I broke one of my two front upper teeth and then, a few days later, the adjacent one, after colliding into the school perimeter wall – the same wall both times! The outcome of these disasters was a series of painful dental procedures and the requirement to wear, for the rest of my life, a cap over each broken front tooth. The initial crowns had been skilfully made by my Uncle John, who was then a dental technician. They were silver and metallic and unfortunately this combination earned me the nickname of 'Choppers'. This, though, was an improvement on 'Hermann the German' and, in a different era, might even have been 'Jaws'. In more recent times, the crowns have been replaced with ceramic ones and the dental surgeons have even managed to match their colour with my existing teeth – as Procol Harum may have sung, 'A Whiter Shade of Green'!

Whilst many of my school friends excelled at the mainstream sports of football and cricket, I did not. I was a fairly good runner though, having practised for most of my young life by sprinting past the various locations in the village where many of the young bully boys hung out. I was once selected to represent the school at an athletics event at the running track of the former British Timken factory in Duston but, on the day I forgot to take my plimsolls and had to do the running in my sandals instead! No designer trainers in those days!

My daily trips to and from school were not always as uneventful as they might otherwise have been. Instead of walking along the proper footpaths in Woodsfield and Frog Hall, I would instead seek out the muddy tracks that had been made along the grass verge on the opposite side of the road. It was here, on the way home from school, that I once made the catastrophic error of losing the small slip of paper which was my end-of-term report. My parents were furious at my carelessness with this vital document and I was sent back to search the roadsides and adjacent fields, but I never found it.

Further down the road, at Frog Hall, opposite the house and farm of the Walters family, was a water source, covered by a locked, rectangular, sloping metallic lid. For some reason, leaping onto this structure appealed to me, that is until the day I slipped in doing so. As I fell I put out my right hand to break my fall and pierced it on the metal hasp which housed a padlock on the lid. A trip to Dr Ewart Thomas, stitches and a tetanus injection followed.

My most endearing humiliation in Year Five at school must surely be my 'starring' role in the school play, 'The Magic Sticks'. This debacle was never forgotten by my friend and fellow performer David 'Kakan' Blake. He writes about it elsewhere in this book!

David and I were considered by Mr Hopkins to be capable of passing the '11 Plus' examination for which we were entered one year in advance of the normal requirement. I remember getting the news that I had passed that examination when I was with my friend David Kipling at his isolated home on Turney's farm, where his father was a manager. David Kipling and David Blake had also passed so we would all be starting at Northampton Grammar School together in September 1957. My parents were delighted at my success and even let me have my birthday present, a brand new scooter, in advance of my tenth birthday. I was to remain at that school until the summer of 1965, and the year 1957 was the start of what turned out to be eight long and largely miserable years for me.

But that is another story!

First Class
David Blake

My first teacher was Mrs Battison and we shared the fact we were both not very tall for our age.

I loved to watch her play the piano and became entranced by the movement of some loose skin under her arms, how it lapped and swayed to the rhythm of gentle melodies, leapt and rippled as she pounded out hymns.

She was gentle, kindness personified, as long as you avoided getting too close to the coke stove that was positioned in the middle of the room, the central heating of its day. The Health and Safety regulation of 1952 was "Get away from that!" No-one scorched in my year.

In Mrs Battison's room I watched, fascinated, as Sonia Clements took out a perfectly white handkerchief, twisted a corner into a point and delicately pushed it up her right nostril, extracted it and replaced it in her pocket. I had never seen such classy behaviour and felt a five year old's flush of first love.

My reading developed at the same gentle rate as Janet and John and dog-eared Nip. My arithme got lots of ticks; I could throw quoits and unknot skipping ropes as well as the next child, unless the next child was Billy Atkinson, of course.

Mrs Battison was good to me, good for me. I remember her with affection.

For me, she was first class.

The School Play
David Blake

The area drama festival was to be held at Moulton Secondary School for all the primary schools in its catchment area. Head teacher Mr Ward Hopkins was determined Brixworth Voluntary Controlled Primary School would give a very good account of itself, and he had chosen as the vehicle for this success a play script based on an Indian folk tale – "The Magic Sticks." In this, the person who steals jewels from the Emperor is exposed by a clever trick devised by the Emperor's Chief Adviser.

The only auditions took place in Ward Hopkins' head, for parts were simply designated at the start of one lesson. When I was 9, I was shy and rather tongue-tied and did not covet a leading role, or indeed any part. There were a few reasonable supporting female roles but the drama hinged on the dynamic of the relationship between the Emperor and the Chief Adviser. David Kipling, he of the received pronunciation and dulcet BBC tones, was, without doubt, an ideal choice for Emperor. Similarly, Michael Hermann, with his matinee idol looks and his clear speaking voice, had the stature and talent to carry off the role of Chief Adviser. He was to be the one on stage most often and with the most lines to deliver.

It turned out that I was to play the adviser's servant and I don't want to "big up my part" but I did have to deliver the key props in the drama. As for my actual lines, they were quite limited. Er, as for my actual line, it was very limited. Mr Ward Hopkins told us to learn our lines within two days and I'd memorised mine before I'd even left the classroom.

Me: (walk on carrying a bundle of sticks)
"I am at your command, O Lord."
Cracked it.

We rehearsed the play for quite a while and no expense was spared in terms of costume because no expense was even considered by the school for costume. However, a photograph from the time shows some parents had made a real effort and the main characters looked impressive. For my role as a mere servant, an old sheet had been fashioned – and I use the word "fashioned" ironically – into what looks like an off-white set of badly manufactured pyjamas. I think a few shepherds from a previous production also turned up in a very slightly altered guise.

As the afternoon of the production approached, Michael, aka as the Chief Adviser, advised the director / head teacher that he had a dental appointment in Northampton on the morning of the festival but would be back in plenty of time for the performance. Mr Ward Hopkins was slightly taken aback by this information but was reassured by Michael's parents' confidence that he would arrive in ample time.

And, true to his word, Michael did arrive at school well before the bus to Moulton was due. No-one, no-one at all, suspected that the morning's appointment had an adverse effect on the Chief Adviser. Perhaps when he was asked to "open wide" it created so great an aperture that previously remembered lines made a rush for the exit.

As soon as the performance began on the massive stage in the cavernous hall of Moulton Secondary School, in front of a considerable audience, it became obvious that there was an under-prepared stand-in playing the part of the Chief Adviser and not Michael Hermann, the word-perfect actor of every rehearsal up to this point. He looked like Michael but he didn't sound like him. In fact, for a while after his first entrance, there was no sound at all. As dramatic pauses go, it was stretching things enormously but then, at last, a voice was heard, but only by those on stage and those seated in rows one to six. I recognised the voice. It was Mrs Burford, the teacher acting as prompter, ensconced in the wings.

"Mighty Emperor, "she said, "I have an idea of how the thief can be caught and your jewels recovered."

"Mighty Emperor," said the boy at centre stage, "I have an idea of how the thief can be caught and your jewels recovered."

The scene jolted into action, with others finally having a chance to speak their lines, and it flowed until another Burford-Hermann echo was required. And another. Er, and another.

Eventually, my moment.

The Chief Adviser announced, "Come, Kakan" and looked stage right as I made my entry from stage left, mumbling, "I am at your command, O Lord" and clutching twelve sticks of identical length.

The play concluded with the thief identified through the adviser's cunning plan involving the sticks, followed by the Emperor's grateful thanks to him, and then polite applause from the audience. Mr Ward Hopkins did not receive the Best Director award but Mrs Burford must have been in the running for Best Supporting Actress.

Michael is still one of my very closest friends and I don't think I should bring up the story of his problem when acting at the Moulton Secondary School Drama Festival of 1957. Nevertheless, I do so - quite often, in fact. Mind you, he is not above summoning me with "Come, Kakan," just to keep me in my rightful place.

It would be really embarrassing for him if the whole episode ever appeared in print.

School play 1957 - the cast

David is standing on the extreme left of the photograph. Michael, with cloak and turban, is kneeling nearby.

School Targets, 1950s Style
David Blake

Mick Bray and Malc Prior
they really, really wanted to be coke monitors,
to delve and dawdle in the dust of the cellar on delivery day,
to fill scuttles
and deliver them to classrooms
in the winter ember months.

Pete Gubbins and Norman Clarke
they really, really wanted to be ink monitors,
to carefully carry big, blue-black bottles
from junior class to junior class,
decanting the precious liquid of learning
into inkwells already packed with screws of blotting paper.
They coveted joining The Esteemed Order of Ink Monitors
(Motto – All's well that ends in well)
members recognisable by their permanent blue hands
and woad - splattered faces.

Me ?
I really, really, really wanted to be
captain of the school football team,
to be picked in front of Geoff, Paul, Tich and Tasty,
who, like me, had already played for two years.

I shot like a centre forward,
tackled like a full back,
passed like a midfielder,
dreamed like an England international.

Instead the Head picked me to enter an exam
a year earlier than I needed to.

I gave it a good shot,
I tackled it as well as I could,
and I passed it, like an idiot.

So I left before my chance to be captain came around.
Left, perhaps because the Head had a target to meet.
Pity no-one bothered to ask me about mine.

On Becoming a 'Grammar Grub'
Michael Hermann

For a timid ten year old who had only ever experienced life in the small village of Brixworth, the changes to my routine on starting grammar school in Northampton were to be quite traumatic. Instead of the familiarity of the walks to school, coming home for a meal at lunchtime and being largely comfortable with my friends, it was necessary to take the number 312 bus to Northampton at around eight in the morning, and then to walk along the Billing Road to arrive at school in time for the regimented entry to the classrooms and the morning assembly. I had to take school dinners, which cost one old shilling for each day, that is five pence today. The return from school at four in the afternoon was via one of the special corporation buses that would take us to St. Giles Street for a fare of one and a half old pence. A short walk down Castilian Street would take us to the Derngate bus station where we could wait for the four fifteen bus home to Brixworth. Should you ever be delayed for any reason, causing you to miss this bus, then the next one to Brixworth was not until five twenty. Parents always knew if you had been kept back at school for a detention.

The toughest challenge for me though was when I realised that all my new schoolmates were older, taller, brighter and far more experienced in the ways of life than myself. In the first year intake there were around one hundred and sixty boys, who were allocated between five classes. Selection to these groups was, I believed, random. David Blake, David Kipling – Kip - and myself found ourselves in different classes, but Kip, in my view, drew the 'short straw' when he found himself in Form 1Y. This was the class of the First Year master, Hugh Eldridge, or 'Hughie' as he was known by the boys. His classroom, Room 23, was separated from the rest of the school and was situated on the opposite side of Billing Road in premises which adjoined the headmaster's home. The entrance to his classroom was via a small cloakroom which housed an old porcelain bath.

I found the headmaster to be an intimidating person. A tall, eccentric, commanding, former intelligence officer with skills in Nordic languages, his icy stare with cold, piercing eyes would turn my legs to jelly. Known by the pupils as 'Stinger', he ran the school as if it were a traditional public school. Discipline was strict and at the smallest issue he could fly into a blinding rage; he was brutal with his canings and once threw a heavy ski boot at an unfortunate pupil who had been summoned to his office for some misdemeanour. We all had to tolerate his searching gaze every morning at assembly, where the whole school gathered in the large hall and surrounding balconies. I pretended to sing the hymns, even when I had forgotten my hymnbook, and I made sure I could never be seen talking to my classmates. If spotted, such an action would lead to him pointing you out. 'You boy – come to my study afterwards!'

In the first week or so of my first term, I encountered the wrath of Stinger when he was in charge of a rugby session for my form. Once on the 'levels' where the pitches were situated, he split us into two teams of fifteen and then ordered one of the groups to change into their white shirts. We had no white shirts – we had not been told by our form teacher to bring any. Stinger flew into an incandescent rage, demanding to know why we did not have our white shirts.

"No-one told us to bring them," said one of the braver lads.

"Who said that?" shouted Stinger, but no-one spoke up.

"I will thrash you all to an inch of your lives unless someone tells me who spoke!"

I was terrified, and the matter did not end there. I remember that a day or two later a lad from our form bravely and unselfishly went to see Stinger to 'own up' on behalf of the class and to end the threat of a group thrashing. I am sure he had not

17

been the culprit on that day and I could not have matched his action.

Another aspect of the new school was a change in the attitude of some of my friends and acquaintances from Brixworth. As only a small number of Brixworth pupils passed the '11 Plus', most of our friends were attending Moulton Secondary Modern School rather than the Grammar Schools or Technical College. Despite growing up in a council estate and sharing very similar lives with our friends, some of us became known as 'Grammar Grubs!'

My lack of enthusiasm for my new schooling arrangements also meant that I rapidly fell behind the rest of my class in my first year studies. Latin, in particular, became a huge challenge for me. The tutor was an elderly, bad tempered gentleman who was known, for obvious reasons, as 'Sarky'.

"Semper, Semper – always in a temper!" was his one and only joke. By a sneaky way of watching reflections in his spectacles, he always knew what was going on behind him as he walked away to the front of a class. Nothing escaped his observation.

Even on the coldest of winter mornings, the Latin class would be held in a very old wooden hut by the side of the Billing Road. It was heated by an ill-smelling coke-fired stove. I hated Latin so much that I decided I would feign illness to avoid having to continue at school. My parents realised this and so my plan did not work. Eventually, during my first year, I genuinely fell ill and needed to be off school for several days.

In each of the termly assessments of school progress, I was normally thirtieth out of thirty one in most subjects. The reports were not pleasant reading for my parents. The end of the third term of the first intake was the time when the 'streaming' for second and subsequent years took place. There were two 'A' streams for the more successful pupils, one for languages and the other for sciences. Then there was a 'B' stream which permitted, for example, the optional study of the German language. For the less able, like myself, there was a 'C' stream and a 'D' stream.

18

David Kipling, the brightest of the three of us from Brixworth, went into an 'A' stream and David Blake, surprisingly, was to join 2D. My fate was to be 2C and I have never understood why David Blake, the smarter of the two of us, did not deserve better. If anything, I was a prime candidate for the 'D' stream. I have my own theories about why this anomaly happened; it could have had something to do with the influence of Hughie.

Unfortunately, during my first year I had come under the 'wing' of Hughie – something that would also happen to my younger brother Peter some years later. He writes at length about his own experiences elsewhere in this book, so I will be brief. In my case, Hughie's predatory approach had started when he befriended my parents. He was once even invited to tea at our house! His offer of extra lessons in mathematics was welcomed by my unsuspecting parents. They did not know that these 'extra lessons', either at Hughie's home or in his classroom, would also be for his own self-gratification. As part of my tuition, very difficult equations were set for me to solve. My failure to get them correct would result in a caning or spanking, followed by a pathetic demonstration of his remorse for my distress. Further details are unnecessary other than to say that things never went beyond this. He also sometimes prowled around my classroom when it was empty. Reading through my schoolwork books, he would seek out untidy or ink-blotted entries, resulting in a command for me to go to see him. These awful sessions and incidents went on for some time until I eventually found the courage to tell my parents and to ask them for it all to stop. I think they were shocked, but they agreed, and I was then at least able to tell Hughie that I would not be attending his private sessions again.

In my second year, the members of Class 2C were inflicted each week with a session of 'double Maths'. This was two lessons rolled into one long one. The teacher was a fiery, ill-tempered man who, on occasions, would fly into a rage and choke on his long, black, wiry moustache. His nickname was 'Smiler' and he was also well practised at aiming a piece of chalk, or even the wooden board eraser, at a pupil. He once opened an upstairs window and, whilst gripping on to a lad's trouser belt, hung him out of the window. Dangerous and terrifying!

One teacher who I remember very well was a Geography and Economics teacher, Mr Harris, known to the pupils as 'Slash.' He was a knowledgeable man who often referred to himself in a slightly self-deprecating manner. If someone was mis-behaving in class, he might say, "I know what's going on - Old Harris is no fool you know." If a detention was awarded, he would write in the register, under the offence, 'Page 6, Rule 10.' That particular entry in the extensive school rule book was the all-embracing 'any breach of common sense is deemed to be a breach of school rules.' Slash also set frequent tests in Geography, ten questions taken from the preparatory reading. One favourite of his was "Do you know the capital of Alaska?" Well, I had the chance of scoring at least one out of ten, Juneau, of course, being the answer.

During my school holidays, I was once in Cambridge with my father. As we were walking through the city, Dad said in a very loud voice, "That chap looks a bit like Old Harris!" To my horror, the gentleman turned around and, yes, it was he! This was not the only time my dad had embarrassed me. There were no mobile phones in those days but he did have a 'Roamer' watch with an alarm. During a performance of a Gilbert and Sullivan operetta in the Grammar School main hall, it sounded off at the most inopportune moment!

My poor motivation and lack of success at school continued until it was time for me to take the 'O' Level examinations in the fifth year. My prospects at this important stage of my academic life were poor. One day, just before the examinations were due to start, on walking into an English class I was surprised to recognise some of my own work emblazoned on the blackboard for all to see. It was a complete paragraph extracted from my last essay submitted as homework. There was not a punctuation mark to be seen and the teacher used this as an example during the lesson as the very worst of written English. Humiliation!

"You are a thumping idiot, Hermann. You will never pass an 'O' Level in English," he announced to the whole class.

I suspected he was correct about my chance of success in the forthcoming examination but I did hope to prove him wrong. Much to my surprise, I did pass, but overall my lack of success in other subjects did not qualify me for entry to the Lower Sixth Form for 'A' Level studies. I, together with David Blake and a few others, repeated the 'O' Level year in the so-called Sixth General whilst the much more successful boys went on to undertake two years in the Sixth Form for their 'A' Levels.

Repeating the 'O' Level year at Northampton was not considered a good thing. Sixth General was looked after by 'Old Harris' and there was an initial lecture to this group of under-performers by Stinger. He informed us that we were here on sufferance and that no poor behaviour on our part would be tolerated; otherwise we faced expulsion from school.

Imagine my fear of what was to come when I again broke one of those school rules by talking to a friend during private study in the library. I was heard by a supervising teacher and awarded a Saturday morning detention. This caused an immediate problem of my having to confess to my parents about why I needed to take a bus to Northampton on Saturday, but also a much more serious matter of how Stinger would react, just a few days after his stern warnings.

Those who were awarded Saturday morning detentions were required to queue up outside Stinger's study each Friday after classes had ended. He would then interrogate each culprit, one by one. When my turn arrived, I answered his "Why, boy, why?" in my trembling voice. I was, of course, expecting to be removed from school. Instead, he chose to double my sentence! Phew – I made sure I never got caught like that again!

After my repeat year, I was deemed able to join the Lower Sixth form and I chose to study Economics and French at 'A' Level and Spanish at 'O' Level. Quite why I selected Economics I will never know. I didn't have a clue what it meant!

But now I began to realise that in two years I would need to get some kind of employment and I knew I needed to work much harder to achieve some adequate qualifications. As it happened, I began to enjoy the subject of Economics and progressed reasonably well. My French class was taken by a very knowledgeable but highly sarcastic master, known to us as 'Spider.' I just hated the thought of being shown up by my incompetence in front of his class and I found myself, for the first time ever, preparing in advance for lessons so that I would be able to deal with the inevitable classroom questioning. The same master took the Spanish lessons and no doubt David Blake will recall bearing the brunt of those sarcastic forces when reading out loud in Spanish. Instead of referring to a character 'Fernando,' he mispronounced it as 'Ferdinando!

"Blake," came the voice from the front of the class, "he's not a prize bull!"

David's ambition to learn Spanish was thus extinguished and he soon dropped the subject.

At some time during my Sixth Form days, I was with my good friend Andrew Bailey in Northampton when we spotted a headline in the local Northampton Chronicle and Echo newspaper. The headmaster of our school, it informed, had plunged his car into Tal-y-lyn Lake in North Wales. We already knew that he had become mentally unstable and had been hospitalised. As it later turned out, his death was recorded as suicide. Such news is not pleasant but to my shame I remember thinking that he would never scare me again.

I have seen many stories and opinions of 'Stinger' from various former pupils. Some liked him and believed him to be fair and thoughtful when dealing with students. Others, like myself, were not so generous.

My academic progress continued to improve until the final stages of my Sixth Upper studies, when just weeks before the 'A' Level examinations I was confined at home with mumps. My neck was swollen and a gradual distortion of the hearing in my left ear turned into a dreadful silence, except, that is, for tinnitus. My left ear had irreversible nerve damage and I would never hear in that ear again. And to add insult to injury, stereophonic music was just becoming available!

Now I had to face oral examinations in French and Spanish with severely impaired hearing. These tests involved a dictation in each of the languages and also an interview conducted with an invited external examiner. The latter was a challenge to say the least. I attempted to compensate by working out a series of standard sentences in each language, such as 'I'm sorry I have not understood the question'! This at least would enable me to say something in the foreign language.

After the examinations I decided to apply for a job as an accountant with the Northampton County Borough Council, without knowing what an accountant actually was! I was interviewed, had an offer subject to examination success, a satisfactory medical and school reference.

When my examination results were announced I was visiting New York, at the home of my father's uncle, Walter. I never received the results that my parents said that they had sent to me and I returned home thinking the worst. In the end I was relieved to discover that my work at school had paid off. I obtained a reasonable grade in French, as well as passes in Economics and Spanish.

I was about to start work and I was delighted that this would mark the end of academia for me.

Or would it?

Going to Big School
Peter Hermann

Starting the Grammar School at Northampton was a time of mixed emotions for me. I was pleased with the success I had achieved by passing the 11 Plus and was encouraged by the very unusual delight expressed by my parents, but there was the ever-present feeling of uncertainty. Would I fit in and would I be able to cope with the requirements of this new and unfamiliar academic life? Socially, matters were also rather strained with my peers, the majority of whom had graduated to the local secondary modern school, and so I endured the chants of 'snob' and 'posh' even though I still lived in the same council estate as my playmates. It was a divisive situation that only got worse as time went by. I was now considered different to my former friends and struggled to maintain the same relationship with many of them that I had enjoyed at the Brixworth village primary school. It was clear, however, that the grammar school was what my parents had set their hearts on for me and being a dutiful son, I embarked upon the adventure, although with wavering courage.

I took comfort from the fact that my brother five years my senior was already at the grammar school and this I considered would afford me a modicum of protection. Indeed, some time ago my brother had received additional maths tuition from the head of Year One, Mr Hugh Eldridge. My parents had once invited him to our house for Sunday tea out of gratitude and so he would be another familiar face.

On the day school was due to start, I awoke early through apprehension, but also with the excitement of trying on my new school uniform, which had to be ordered from a specialist supplier at huge expense. Everything, including the grey long socks, was the customary one size too big. My mother's explanations being that, for the reasons of economy, as a growing boy, I would soon fit into them. She had saved the money for my uniform, earned by plaiting strands of leather at home for a local shoe manufacturer. She was paid six pence a yard and one can only imagine how many miles of leather must have passed through her calloused and arthritic fingers to pay for the compulsory demands made by the Boys' Grammar School. In addition to the uniform, there was the additional expense of the obligatory blue tracksuit, gym kit, white cricket flannels and school rugby shirts, all prerequisites for this all-male domain.

The oversized uniform itself consisted of navy blazer complete with embroidered crested badge, grey shorts, white shirt, and a tie with navy and claret diagonal stripes. The crowning glory to this 'ensemble' was the peaked cap in size six and three quarters, which school rules dictated was to be worn until the Fifth Form, when we would be rising sixteen year olds. The cap itself, which at first rested for support upon my ears, bending them forward to give me a rather comical appearance, immediately became a point of ridicule to others and an annoyance to me. This pristine cap, together with the short trousers - long ones could be worn from Year Two - singled us out as 'new boys' and we at once became the sport of the older and more established members of the historic establishment I had recently joined. Furthermore, no other education institution in the area at that time insisted on its pupils wearing caps and it visually identified us to members of the public that we were indeed a 'race apart,' members of the elite, the privileged ones who, blessed with the necessary 'grey matter', had passed the rigours of 'the test' to claim membership to that roll of honour, 'the grammar school'. My only other necessary accoutrement was a rather large, stiff, leather satchel which hung suspended from my bony shoulders. This contained a new pencil case, which, for now, rattled around in the otherwise vacant interior of this cavernous accessory.

The morning journey to school was made on a double-decker bus at seven forty five, followed by a walk of some one and a half miles from the town centre. Along this route, the newly starched white collar of my shirt was to chaff my neck, new ill-fitting rigid black leather shoes were to rub my ankles and the now book-laden heavy satchel was to bash against my bare legs as it swung heavily by my side. For the first week or so we 'new boys' were fair game for the initiation process inflicted on us by the older boys of the school who would gather around us menacingly. Caps were the trophies they sought. The prized headgear would be snatched from your head, usually with a few strands of hair, and passed between the gathering crowd, like a rugby ball. Meanwhile, the victim found himself jumping up and down, squealing like a 'piggy in the middle,' trying to retrieve the cap before it was deposited in a muddy puddle, accompanied by screeches of delight as the culprits ran off in search of further prey. There was no safety even if we walked in large groups and there was no point in complaining to the 'masters' as this process was considered a 'rite of passage' and covertly encouraged by staff and prefects alike. So one learned the hard way. Once approached, the best method was to outrun, swerve or dodge your attackers, holding on to your cap whilst it was still on your head, as it was a punishable offence to be seen without a cap in public.

During the bus journey itself, caps would be grabbed from your head; they might be thrown from the front to the back of the bus, hidden, burnt with cigarettes, or even dangled out of the bus windows, holding you to ransom for snacks, sweets or money. Life was indeed precarious for an eleven year old and, needless to say, after a few weeks the cap began to look very battle-scarred and the once spotlessly immaculate school uniform became dishevelled, having suffered from acid burns in the science lab or being subjected to the ever-present hostilities, scuffles and fights with other boys. After a while, life did settle down and, being more confident, we took to arranging our caps in an increasingly jauntier fashion upon our heads.

Lunch time breaks at the new school were a real source of danger for any new boy. We were hijacked in the cloakrooms and our blazer pockets rifled. With legs dangling and screaming for mercy, we would be suspended by our blazer collars on the swan-neck pegs of the changing room. Here we would remain until we were either released or our metal buttons gave way. The copse at the rear of the school was another place to avoid. This was accessed by a number of 'levels', each one containing a rugby pitch and separated by a grassy bank. Gangs of older boys would hide in the woods ready to ambush any new boy. We knew this was another part of the initiation process and any sensible boy would have stayed in the playground under the relative protection and supervision of the prefects. The more adventurous of us, however, could not resist the thrill of running that gauntlet of older boys who lay in ambush armed with small white squidgy berries that would be applied to our heads to give us 'an egg shampoo'.

"First formers!! Let's scrag 'em!!" The cry would go up from the hidden second and third formers concealed in the thicket.

"Quick, let's go, run for it!" we would shout in panic as the physically larger boys made their whereabouts known and began the pursuit. We would run, only to get separated and brought to the ground by a crunching, well-aimed rugby tackle, ending in the ceremonial 'egging' process. Once released, we would run off until, at a secure distance, we would taunt the older boys with names such as Fatty, Spotty or Four Eyes. At the end of the day I would return home, tired, bruised, hair stiff with berry juice, cap soaked, and blazer muddied.

For me, however, it wasn't the school lunch breaks that were the significant problem as every other new boy suffered the same. The work in class presented me with an even greater challenge. From day one, I struggled and faltered at every step.

27

This was a new dilemma for me. I began to detest the whole process. Most of all I feared those sharp - tongued, black-gowned masters. They called you by your surname or more impersonally 'boy'. Sarcasm ruled the day and you were made to feel uncomfortable and insignificant. How I began to dislike those nefarious 'rook-like' creatures as they strutted through the corridors in flapping gowns, book in hand, crowing about the merits of a classical education. There were tests, positional rankings and the inevitable scorn in the termly reports for the ensuing and predictable failures. I considered myself to be less academic and more practical, creative and artistic. I had always enjoyed all types of sport but even our weekly outings to the often frozen or waterlogged rugby pitch brought no further solace. For here, surrounded by more mature boys, they would relish in pummelling and bruising my diminutive body at every encounter with the oddly-shaped ball as it twisted and turned during play. The cross-country run through the icy, knee - deep local flood plain did nothing to inspire or replenish my wanting soul and I longed to be allowed to play football again. Something had to change, I thought.

I was prepared to go to any lengths to arrest my feelings of utter despair. In a desperate attempt to gain some respite, I contrived to hatch a plan to end this misery. Over the course of several weeks, I presented myself to my parents as having the most excruciating stomach pains. I was examined by my G.P., Dr Thomas, who diagnosed that nothing serious was amiss and prescribed liquid paraffin for my bowel. I continued to complain and begged to be allowed to stay at home. The occasional day's absence further damaged my faltering academic progress and resulted in me falling further and further behind my peers. Finally, after several further visits to Dr Thomas, I was eventually referred to a consultant at the hospital who confirmed that I may have grumbling appendicitis. Success had been achieved and I would need an operation. I was ecstatic. The daily spoonful of liquid paraffin administered religiously by my mother would mercifully now end. I would miss the end-of-term school examinations. The timing was perfect, or so I thought...

At hospital I was cut open, to reveal, I am certain, a perfectly healthy and normal appendix. The operation itself necessitated a week in hospital and two weeks of painful recovery at home, but this was sufficient recompense to spare me from the emotional agony of the day-to-day onslaught that heralded the waning of my intellectual and sporting powers.

So it was that after my operation and reluctantly being packed off to school again, I decided that I had no other option but to try a little harder. During this spree of conscientious application to my studies, I also took an opportunity to better myself socially, as I misguidedly thought. I joined the elocution lessons - affectionately known as 'electrocution' - which were arranged at lunch time by the head of Year One, Mr Eldridge, who was referred to by us boys as 'Hughie'. What a mistake I had unwittingly made.

"Right, Brixworth," - Hughie referred to us by our place of residence – "stand up and count to ten." The erudite and eloquent black-gowned Hughie smoothed his short greying hair with his hand.

I composed myself. "One, two, three, four, five, six, seven, eight, niane, ten," I said, slowly, in my poshest voice. This was accompanied by howls of laughter from my assembled peers.

"Now do it again, Brixworth," Hughie requested, without any correction or any indication as to why my contemporaries had found my rendition so amusing.

"One, two, three, four, five, six, seven, eight, niane..."

Before I could complete the allotted task, I was overtaken by more laughter from the class who, appreciating Hughie's little joke at my expense, conjoined with him there and then.

"Do it again," he sighed, this time accompanied by squeals of delight from my counterparts.

"What telephone number, might I ask, would one ring to summon an ambulance, boy?"

I stood before him, frozen. There was no escape. How I hated him now and was regretting joining the rotten class. 'Did he laugh at my Dad's foreign accent that time when he had graced our tea table?' I thought angrily. Hughie was enjoying every aspect of my ridicule.

"Well, Brixworth, I assume, boy, that you are familiar with the use of a telephone," goaded Hughie. The class laughed then fell silent, eagerly waiting my response. How I despised Hughie as my cheeks flushed for the third time at my inability to disguise my local accent.

"Niane, niane niane," came the parroted response, this time embellished with thumps on the desks, guffaws and genuine tears of laughter from both friend and foe gathered in the classroom.

"I see we have work to do, boy. What time do we commence morning prayers?"

With relief, I answered truthfully, "Eight fifty five a.m., sir."

"Very clever, boy," came Hughie's response. "Not five to niane?" questioned Hughie mockingly, trying to obtain one more laugh to my expense.

It was apparent, however, that Hughie was fond of some of us little boys and he had his favourites. Bare inside thighs peeking out from grey flannel shorts would be patted affectionately by the small hands of the diminutive but overweight master as he corrected our work at his desk.

Some days later, early in the day, I was approached by Hughie as I arrived at the school gate.

"Right, Brixworth! Not wearing your cap outside school premises. Oh dear! Oh dear! Come to my room at four p.m. prompt," Hughie commanded.

"But... but, sir, those boys have snatched it, sir. I have a bus to catch at four fifteen," I tried to reason.

"Don't argue with me, boy!" he roared,.

After retrieving my cap, I spent the rest of the day worried and anxious. I did not want to go to Hughie's room alone. I had heard the rumours from older boys who called him by the derogatory and politically incorrect term 'homo'. I knew what that meant – even then. I turned over in my mind all the possible solutions to my dilemma. I could pretend I had forgotten and present myself early the next day just as class was assembling. Perhaps, I thought, he might forget the arrangement and I could arrive early and leave a note.

Full of fear, my mind in turmoil, I arrived at Hughie's form room deliberately earlier than the appointed time in the hope that some other boys may still be present. Regrettably, the room was empty of people, save for Hughie who, unfortunately for me, had only too well remembered our 'rendezvous'. He sat at his desk, ensconced in a chalk-dust soiled gown, waiting for me, busying himself with tidying his papers. A pile of exercise books stood on the corner of the huge wooden desk next to a large black slip-on plimsoll.

Without a greeting, he picked up the slipper, flexed it with both hands and waved it mockingly in front of my terrified face. His own appearance demonstrated the contentment and pleasure of the power he was able to wield over me.

"Over the desk!" he barked.

Not wishing to miss my bus and have to confess to my mother why I was late, I compliantly bent over without delay, hoping to get the unpleasant ordeal over with as soon as possible. I stayed in that undignified and vulnerable position for what seemed like an eternity, feeling the smooth wood grain of the desk with my palms, anticipating the pain and torment to come. At any moment the sharp twang of rubber slipper would connect with my now tightened and clenched buttocks. I was aware of Hughie standing behind me. Still no pain was forthcoming, but I did not dare to look round for fear of antagonising him.

31

'Get on with it,' I thought, 'I want to go home.'

After a full five minutes of bending over that desk waiting for the spanking to commence, Hughie said in a kinder voice, "Okay Brixworth, you can go."

"Thank you, sssir, thank you," I stammered in relief, unable to believe that he had not touched me at all with either slipper or hand. Without hesitating, I grabbed my satchel, repositioned my cap and bolted, crying tears of relief, all the way to the relative safety of the school bus. After those events, except for the compulsory weekly divinity lesson, I took to avoiding Hughie at every opportunity, absenting myself too from the weekly Friday elocution class.

Fortunately, after the events of that day Hughie's interest in me seemed to wane and, as he only taught first formers, during my later years at the school our paths were never to cross again. I must, however, have provided Hughie with a thrill that day, and gazing at my pert young bottom stretched over his old oak desk was all the gratification that he needed.

I had been lucky that day in Hughie's form room but I often wondered how many other boys might have been less fortunate.

Early Days

Brixworth Church Choirboys

Peter is front central, with Michael peering over his head. It was a ruff time for all of us.

The Winter of 1947
David Blake

I suffer from Seasonal Affective Disorder. It's SAD, I know. If I had my choice I would hibernate from November to late March. When the squirrels in the park start making sure their nuts are stowed safe and warm for the winter months, I go home and check the condition of my long johns.

The reason for my Seasonal Affective Disorder? Well, I was born in the winter of 1947 – yes, the legendary, tremendously harsh winter of 1947. Winter? It was more like an ice age, with months of sub-zero temperatures and sudden and dramatic snowfalls.

I was due in February but was actually born in April, deciding to stay in the warm for as long as possible. Conditions were awful and there were obviously lots of practical problems in bringing up a family in such circumstances. For one thing, it was very difficult to keep the house warm. Dad had already chopped two legs off the dining room table, to be burnt on the fire, and it was a lean time in terms of food.

Dad made the decision that he would venture out on an expedition in an attempt to find extra wood for the fire. He would take the family sledge, which my brother Bob had named Percy.

Dad took quite a while to prepare his clothing. My mum told him we ought to wear a hat that covered his ears. She was hinting at a balaclava. That went right over his head.

He put on a heavy woollen sweater that my gran had knitted him for Christmas. It had a motif of hens. Dad knew that in cold weather it is best to wear lots of layers.

Unfortunately for our family pet, Minnie, a pedigree mongrel, he decided he needed some fur-lined gloves. Dad was rather haphazard in his shearing so several parts of the dog's coat looked more appropriate for warmer weather. Really, it was only a winter's tail.

Dad had his legs lagged with the material that normally protected the water pipes from freezing. Over that, he wore his golfing trousers, as he knew he would have to walk a fairway and he wanted to be back by tea time.

He put on his old RAF great coat, which was being used as a bed cover. Then, in an attempt to recreate an illustration from the book *Nanook of the Frozen North*, he tied a tennis racquet under each of his wellingtons, as rudimentary snow shoes.

Before stepping out into the Antarctic landscape on the fateful day, Dad had a breakfast of Scott's Porridge and, after Oates, announced, "I am going outside. I may be some time."

"Farewell," he said, in a gruff voice. He thought it might help him pull the sledge if he was a little husky.

He set off into the wind in the wild, white winter land that was Spratton Road in Brixworth. It was very difficult going, given the weather conditions and his ill-advised footwear. Progress was very slow indeed. Persevering, despite Percy veering, he trudged along the length of the road and at the end of the village had the choice of three directions.

He decided to turn right into the part of the village known as Frog Hall. This was appropriately named as he found absolutely nothing. The temperature was bitterly cold and he just had to stop for a Slazenger. It had come loose from his welly. He then headed towards Church Street and the magnificent Saxon church of All Saints.

Eventually he did notice something in the snow ahead of him. It was a small, domed, black object. He rushed towards it as quickly as conditions allowed and saw it was the top of a man's bowler hat. He knelt down, took off his gloves and scrabbled away at the snow until he revealed the complete brim. He decided to lever it out of the snow and with considerable effort prised up the hat. And there beneath was the top of a man's head!

Giving no thought to the biting chill in his fingers, Dad then worked feverishly to remove snow from around the man's head, his eyes, nose and mouth. When this was done, Dad said, "Don't worry, I'll go and get a spade."

The man said, "Make it a long one – I'm riding a horse."

That was the winter of 1947 and I know all of this is true because my dad told it to me.

Codin's Cap
David Blake

I'm going to recount something that happened when I was 9 and has stayed with me to this day. You see, I know what happened to Codin's cap.

The buildings of the primary school I went to are still there, nestled beneath All Saints Church in Brixworth. It's now a community centre. And you'll need to know about an alleyway in the village, a short cut to school. It was officially called Pond Close but to us it was Ponky.

Ponky began near the school, close to the Buttercross, and ran between high walls. Over the wall to the left there were the Hall grounds, with fine houses and a pond. I don't know what sort of people lived there but they had to keep them behind walls that had cement on top of the stonework decorated with shards of glass. The wall on the right was just as high at the start of Ponky but towards the bottom of the slope dropped to waist height. Over on that side there was a lovely bungalow with sweeping lawns and manicured gardens. Near the stream that bubbled out from under the alley's path, the owners had left the garden to grow naturally wild, so there were reeds, grasses and bushes.

Ponky was a cut-through but it was also used for bike racing. The kids would start from the No Cycling sign at the top and finish at the No Cycling sign at the bottom. And at weekends it seems to have been the venue for a balloon modelling club, as on most Mondays on our walk to school we would find strange elongated balloons, obviously failed attempts to create balloon models of dachshunds.

I said I know what happened to Codin's cap. Codin wasn't the lad's real name. One September we had a new teacher and it was one of those back-to-school days when new exercise books were given out. "Write your name on" was the instruction and the teacher circulated whilst we did so. He leant over one pupil.

"What does that say, boy?"

"Colin Butler," said the pupil.

"Looks more like Cod in Batter to me."

Suppressed hilarity in the class.

So from that day forth, Colin was Codin – but never in his hearing! I was over a year younger than him and short for my height whereas he was very tall for his. And he was not the most pleasant personality – he could hear sweet papers rustling fifty yards away and would purloin the goodies. Codin was a poker, a pusher, a pugilist. I steered well clear.

One summer's afternoon I wanted to get back home quickly – I can't remember why – and once we'd been dismissed I rushed to the cloakroom and grabbed my coat from the top peg. I set off down Ponky and towards the bottom of the slope I swapped the coat from one hand to the other. As I did so, something dropped to the ground. It was a cap.

Oh! I must have plucked it from the peg below mine. The peaked cap was an awful design of concentric green and red circles with a button in the middle. From above it looked like a target, so not the sort of thing you'd want to wear in Trafalgar Square. I picked it up and turned it over. It was obviously new, there were no grease stains inside and the name label was pure white, except for where the name had been inked in. My heart sank. The name was Colin Butler. Codin!

So there I was in Ponky and I pictured the owner searching the cloakroom for his missing cap, perhaps not being in the best of moods. I would go back up to school, walk in and say, "Colin, by mistake I just happened to have..." POW! SPLAT. My eyes started watering at the mere thought of it. I didn't like Plan A; there must be a Plan B that didn't involve any physical pain for me. Of course! Every day I walked home past Codin's house so I could fold the cap and post it through the letter box. He'd come

38

home and be amazed that his cap had been returned by some mysterious passer-by. A great plan, except that every time I had walked past his house Mrs Butler had been at the window, awaiting the return of her beloved son. So I'd be seen posting the cap, Codin would come home and be informed that David Blake had delivered it, and the next morning near school - POW! SPLAT! There must be a Plan C.

I looked round. Still no-one else was in sight. I knew Codin always came down Ponky. I decided to simply place the cap on the lowest bit of wall. He would arrive later and go, "Oh, look, there's my cap. I wonder how that got there. What a mystery! Still, at least I have it back." I liked Plan C....no POW! SPLAT! - so I had a last check that I was not being seen and left the cap on the wall at the bottom of the alleyway.

I ran home as fast as my chubby little legs would carry me and already Plan C didn't seem such a great idea, judging by the guilty thoughts buzzing around my head. Still, the deed was done and I raced into my house, swiftly shutting the door behind me. Sanctuary. But Mum was there and I'm the youngest of seven children so Mum knew kids.

"What's the matter with you?" she asked.

"Nothing," I said.

"You look hot and bothered." Mum had her own special way of checking for temperatures and any sign of illness. It involved plonking her hand on your forehead. Thus, a large palm slapped onto my brow.

"You feel very warm. Are you sure you're okay?"

"Yes, Mum," I insisted, "it's only 'cause I ran home."

"And why did you run home? You don't usually run home."

"I just wanted to, that's all."

The interrogation continued. "Has anything bad happened at school?"

"No," I said, and that was true. The bad thing had happened at Ponky. Mum let things be, for a time.

I wasn't ill as such but I was having an acute attack of conscience, and I definitely didn't feel hungry enough to tackle the portions of food placed in front of me at five o'clock.

A huge hand landed on my forehead. "You're not eating much. What's the matter with you?"

"Nothing."

I spent the rest of the evening regretting my actions. What if I'd have taken the cap straight back and Codin had just said thanks?

Night-time was the worst. I shared a bed with brother Paddy. No way could I get to sleep and I soon heated up the central part of my portion of the bed. I swung my legs over to the right and soon heated up that side. The left didn't take too long either and, of course, that was close to someone else's territory.

"Stop wriggling about, boy!"

I pummelled the pillows into submission but still had no place to comfortably rest my head. Every time I turned over, the blankets wrestled with me, putting me into holds with which Codin would have been pleased. I was fearful of what the dawn may bring, despite the fact I was sure I hadn't been seen, and, eventually exhaustion took over, my eyes finally closed and...

"PADDY, DAVID, TIME TO GET UP!"

Oh no! Morning! Usually I was one of the very first in the playground, ready to get the football game going, but not today. Today I was a very reluctant pupil and walked slowly the long way to school, avoiding a certain person's house and a certain alleyway. I waited by the Buttercross until I saw the teacher on duty come out with the bell and then ran up the steps into the playground, joining my class line at the very end. Codin was near the front. As I was completely incapable of hiding my guilt, I had chosen to avoid having any eye contact with him all day. Thus when he turned towards where I was standing, I bent down to do up my shoelace.

We were in the same class and things got extremely difficult when we sat down. I found myself rocking backwards, forwards and sideways, and sometimes all three, in order to get other people to block him from seeing me. I also got lower and lower in my chair so that my chin was only just above desk level. Then it was assembly time.

The partition between the junior classrooms was opened, desks and chairs were pushed to one side, and the infants joined us as we sat, cross-legged and squashed. I managed to get on the opposite end of the line to Codin and continued my routine of ducking and leaning to avoid his glance. My dry mouth meant I mimed through the hymns and prayers and assembly was over. Or so I thought, but the head teacher Mr Ward Hopkins had an announcement to make. He took an envelope out of his inside pocket.

"Children," he began, "I have a letter here from Mrs Butler, Colin's mother."

I gulped.

"Colin recently had a new cap..." My face glowed bright red. "...It went missing from the cloakroom yesterday. This is not the sort of thing we expect in our school. Does anyone know anything about it?"

I felt as if there was an enormous arrow suspended from the ceiling above my head with flashing neon letters spelling out the words "IT'S HIM." I just couldn't understand why he hadn't found the cap.

Another decision to make. I could put up my hand and say, "Yes, sir. It was me, sir. I took the cap by mistake and left it on a wall in the village." But that didn't sound very good inside my head and I was sure it wouldn't if it was said aloud. So I kept quiet about it, and I have ever since, until today.

The rest of that day dragged. You won't be surprised to hear that my temperature was checked at home for the next couple of days. I was very relieved when, a few weeks later, Codin left to go

41

to secondary school and I managed, for a while, to push the event to the back of my mind.

It was almost a year later when vivid memories flooded back. I was playing hide-and-seek near Ponky and naughtily thought a good place to hide was over the wall and in the growth around the stream. I clambered over, pushed my way through some reeds and came to a sudden halt.

There, in a bush, about two feet up from the ground, was hanging a piece of cloth, green and red in colour. In an instant I knew what it was. What I couldn't grasp was how it came to be here, five yards in from the wall on which I had left it. I ceased my trespassing and climbed back into Ponky, giving myself up to the seeker, my head full of questions.

It hadn't been a windy day when I left the cap and anyway it would have needed a very strong wind to lift it and blow it that far. The only explanation I can think of is that the cap was seen by one of the next people to come down Ponky. Perhaps they, like me, had turned it over and seen the name. Perhaps they had been at the receiving end of some of Codin's treatment and saw a way to get a little revenge. Perhaps they had used the cap like a frisbee and skimmed it into the undergrowth.

I don't know - it's only guesswork. That may not be what happened. But I think there's someone else who, like me, can say, "I know what happened to Codin's cap."

Pond Close, Brixworth (Ponky)

The lower wall on the right-hand side, where the path turns to the right, identifies where Codin's cap was initially placed.

If Music Be the Food of Love…
Peter Hermann

My musical life began at a young age and centred around the church where I was soon to be enrolled as a choir boy. This is not to say that I had the celestial voice of an angel. Far from it! Having a good singing voice was never a pre-requisite when you volunteered to join the church choir. For some reason, there was always a shortage of boys and girls of my age willing to participate in this religious pursuit. Indeed, few youngsters with the necessary spiritual conviction were prepared for the commitment of relinquishing two to three hours on a Sunday as well as the obligatory Friday night choir practice. The chorister's apparel of black cassock, a white surplus and a frilly starched collar was less than flattering and far from the Carnaby Street styles to which we 'near teens' longingly aspired. However, that apart, the reward of sixpence a service and as much as half a crown for a wedding was incentive enough for me. Thus I began my first paid employment at the age of ten and the only criteria, as far as I was concerned, for being a member of that holy group was your willingness to turn up and a public demonstration of correct 'choral behaviour' in keeping with the privileged pious position. There was no audition or application process and we were to become a mixed bunch of male and female vocal misfits of all shapes and sizes, under the very strict guidance of Mr Carroll, the church organist and choir master.

Mr Carroll himself did not manifest the necessary personality or attractive features to inspire and motivate us budding sopranos. He was a rather short, balding and rotund character with little piggy eyes which were shielded by small, round-rimmed spectacles perched upon a large red bulbous nose. His teaching style and demeanour towards us also lacked refinement and his deficiency in stature also extended to his temper, which was often very irascible.

Mr Carroll was to have no success with the training of my rather inadequate and temperamental voice box. It squeaked, cracked and croaked, soaring uncontrollably into warbled crescendos of flat note upon flat note. My best friend Marcus's voice, on the other hand, was one of perfect pitch and Mr Carroll, who worked with Marcus's father at 'the council offices,' seemed to worship and adore him for it. He nurtured Marcus's voice as if it was a tender young plant. Marcus would be singled out at every choir practice for immeasurable praise which beggared belief. Moreover, Mr Carroll was to use the exemplar of his fine-tuned soprano voice to heap scorn and derision upon the rest of us failing 'raggle taggle band' of youngsters. Marcus was, of course, to sing all the solo pieces, whilst those with less than dulcet tones would look on with resentment, being forced to the back row of the stalls during any public proceedings.

The highlight of the choral year was the Christmas carol singing. We would be encouraged to make our own lanterns from jam jars, sticks and candles; we would wrap up warmly and meet at the Vicarage at six sharp. All of us juveniles loved it and, although prepared with several layers of socks, our toes were to freeze to death, our jam jars would crack and our candles would burn out by seven.

The village contained some very large houses occupied by wealthy people. Although we would visit every area of the village, knock on doors with our collecting boxes and stand in the street and 'sing our little hearts out', these larger houses were singled out for special visits. Whereas the ordinary houses would afford us a few 'coppers' or even 'silver' coins to swell our little boxes, the larger establishments would produce 'paper' money. Here we would reverently remove our hats and assemble around the fire or Christmas tree and sing a selection of carols for the assembled household and their guests. Our reward would be a warming glow from the fire, a cup of orange squash and a mince pie, whilst the adults would imbibe mulled wine, sherry or home-made punch.

After several of these special visits, the adults would become a little fuller of 'the cup of human kindness.' Mr Carroll himself would almost be seen to smile as we viewed his larger-than-life, protruding nose, glowing even redder by the light of our lanterns. On one occasion, we had assembled in the hall of a large house, complete with its suits of armour and heraldic shields, and after more sherry and mince pies, we began our repertoire in front of a roaring log fire. Feeling somewhat chilled by the cold night air, I had made my way to the front of the gathering, standing shoulder to shoulder with Marcus. Mr Carroll was conducting us from the front, facing us and counting us in, waving his short over-coated arms and using facial expressions to try and illicit the best in us. Marcus's voice was in fine form yet again that evening and, encouraged by Mr Carroll's now unusually smiling face, I began to imitate Marcus. The continued look of my now 'beloved' choirmaster's face seemed proof to me that, at last, my musical career was taking off. Indeed, Mr Carroll, now glowing in the warmth of that log fire, was positively beaming with delight and raising his hands encouraging us to sing louder and louder. This I instinctively did, blasting out the chorus of 'Oh Come All Ye Faithful' at a deafening pitch, whilst smiling back at Mr Carroll, my face radiantly happy with my new-found approval. Soon Mr Carroll's face turned to a frown and I knew something was amiss. Was it me? Surely not, I'm singing fine now. I searched Mr Carroll's face for further signs of endorsement. Mr Carroll stopped his conducting with one of his hands and whilst staring angrily at my troubled face placed a large podgy finger to his wine-wet lips, using his other hand to encourage Marcus even more to swell to a crescendo.

'Oh, he does mean me,' I thought. I was crestfallen, deeply hurt by Mr Carroll's gesture and also embarrassed by my naivety. I

46

had failed again, I concluded. I now detested Mr Carroll for his lack of faith in my ability and I was again immeasurably jealous of Marcus and 'his voice'. I began to brood over my inner turmoil, to contemplate and examine my friendship with Marcus. I hated him as much as I despised Mr Carroll!

To make things better, I intended, if possible, to improve in private the acceptability of my voice. I therefore took to growing my dark hair into a fashionable 'Beatle Fringe' and proceeded to sing in front of the bathroom mirror. Complete with a 'pretend' microphone using my mother's discarded hair brush, I sang 'She Loves You, Yer, Yer, Yer' at every possible opportunity, much to the annoyance of all my family. Publicly, however, I was to adopt another strategy. I may as well look the part if I can't sound like a choir boy, I resolved. So, for the rest of my career as a chorister, I was to mime, and I became very skilful at this deception, safe in the knowledge that I was only there to swell the numbers.

Nevertheless, music did continue to play an important part in my early life. I would spend hours with my father in our dining room, listening to classical music which he would play from large 78 rpm, 12-inch records on an enormous wooden 'His Master's Voice' gramophone player. Scratches, jumps and slips were commonplace, but the sound was satisfying enough for the era. I was to learn about composers from my father's homeland of Czechoslovakia and I grew to love those special winter evenings listening to Smetana and Dvořák. My father was also an accomplished pianist and he would perform for me on our old upright pianoforte. Keen to emulate my father's skill, I pleaded with him to teach me how to master the instrument. Instead, lessons were arranged, with Mr Carroll the choir master.

My lessons began with great enthusiasm on my part. I quickly mastered the notes for the right hand very well and in no time at all I could read music and play a simple tune. I would walk to the lessons to be held at Mr Carroll's stone terraced cottage in the older part of the village. I would arrive at the door of the cottage a few minutes early and hear 'The Moonlight Sonata' being played beautifully by Lawrence who had the hour-long session from 6 pm.

'I wish I could play like that,' I used to think as I sat on the small stone wall next to Mr Carroll's door. As Lawrence came through the door carrying his beautiful leather music manuscript case at the end of his session, I reflected, though, that I didn't want to be a 'sissy' like him. He can't even kick a ball or ride a bike!

By the time three or four of my lessons had passed, I had taken to folding my own 'Boosey and Hawkes' piano music book into four to produce a small square, enabling it to fit comfortably into the inside pocket of my duffle coat. This was considered a necessity, as thus concealed, it would then avoid any embarrassment from the inquisition by the older local boys from my council estate who gathered each evening on the street corner. Imagine what derision and punishment the sight of a music book would have evoked in them. 'Best not give them anything to laugh at,' I thought.

Mr Carroll lived alone, and it was well known that he loved a drink or two at The George Inn. On arrival at his house and with him sitting next to me at the piano, his breath would always smell faintly of sweet sherry. I would play my practised piece and Mr Carroll would tap the rhythm out with a pencil. All went well and he seemed more pleased with my playing ability than my singing. I practised and practised. I didn't find the left hand so easy to master, however, and my progress began to slow. Occasionally, I would have moments of sheer brilliance, or so I thought, only to find that Mr Carroll would show his disapproval with 'tuts' and shakes of his large head. He would play the piece for me and even I had to admit that the two renditions sounded like completely different tunes.

I continued to find it very hard to co-ordinate the left with the right hand. My brain became confused and jumbled. I could play a melody, but at times there were gaps as my fingers twitched and hovered seemingly endlessly, as if suspended in time, as I searched frantically for the right notes to play. Lessons came to be something to dread and I practised less and less. I wanted to stop lessons now and I began to hate 'sissy' Lawrence as his accomplished playing was now what I considered to be 'concert status'.

I plodded on, encouraged by my father. However, I dreaded every Tuesday night, fearing what Mr Carroll would say about my lack of skill and insufficient practice. By this time, my music manuscript was beginning to look a sorry sight but fortunately I was able to pass to the next stage and a new book was requisitioned. It took no time at all, however, to convert the large pristine manuscript into a small 'tatty novel' to hide my secret pursuit from unwanted attention.

Several months into the new book, progress was again beginning to stagnate. By comparison, sitting on that bumpy low wall outside the cottage, Lawrence appeared to me to be on his 'second world tour' with the London Philharmonic Orchestra. Mr Carroll's patience with me continued to wane. He smelled more and more of drink, probably taken in the interlude after Lawrence's departure, to fortify himself against the cacophony that was to follow. After I had treated him to my practised piece, he took to disappearing into the back kitchen and then walking around the small living room holding his large balding head in his hands. By this time, completely frustrated by my inability to find the correct notes, he had also taken to tapping my straying fingers with his pencil. I now knew I was failing badly.

Sitting on that wall waiting for my lesson, Lawrence's playing continued to irk me more and more and this was to become the status quo for week after week. Lawrence was a genius, I had to admit, and Mr Carroll had taken to telling me so. The usual disapproval of his 'tuts' and shakes of his head continued each lesson. Despite my efforts to please, there was little

49

encouragement and no praise. 'Tap, tap tap!' went that pencil in rhythm of the piece once more and then, one day, a final vicious down-stroke of the pencil cracked my knuckle on the beat so hard that I winced with pain. I hated that piano and I hated Mr Carroll. I slammed the piano lid on his hands. He was shocked. Then I stood, grabbed at my tattered book, turned and fled without looking back, slamming the heavy oak house door behind me.

"I'm not going back!" I wailed as I arrived home. I flung the dishevelled manuscript book across the lounge floor causing its tattered pages to fly into the air like giant confetti, much to the excitement of our barking puppy dog.

"What do mean, not going back?" enquired my surprised father.

"He hits me with a pencil, and it hurts and I'm not going back!" I screamed. I didn't tell Dad that I had slammed the lid down on his hands. He found that out the next day from Mr Carroll. Dad was furious with me. I was told to apologise to Mr Carroll and I reluctantly agreed. I delayed for a few days, feeling frightened about what he would say.

But then I heard that Mr Carroll had suffered a brain haemorrhage at work. He died in hospital the next day and my carefully rehearsed apology was never delivered. I attended his funeral and stood over his grave, bowing my head in shame as they threw earth on his coffin, thinking that I was somehow responsible for his death.

After his funeral, as one of his pupils, I was allowed to choose one or two small items from Mr Carroll's possessions. The executor of the estate, Mr Hadland, asked me to meet him at Mr Carroll's house several weeks after the funeral. Evoking that all too familiar feeling of trepidation, I once again crossed the threshold of the small stone cottage. With my heart pounding and my mouth dry with guilt and anxiety, I gave a sideways and somewhat perfunctory glance at the offending piano. I was somehow responsible for all this, I thought, as I ventured further into the darkened and eerie room, half expecting the ghost of Mr Carroll to appear from his small back kitchen.

My eyes now accustomed to the gloom eventually rested upon the familiar and smiling face of Mr Hadland. Reassured, I looked around the room and there on the small table in the middle of the room, resided a small selection of Mr Carroll's most precious possessions. Before me, twinkling in the sunlight that shone through a tiny chink in the curtains, lay a small silver pen knife, complete with a mother of pearl handle.

"Please may I have this? Please," I managed to utter. Hardly waiting for an answer, I turned and fled as quickly as possible, out into the revitalizing sunlight, clutching the penknife tightly in the palm of my hand.

I use it to this day but never to sharpen my pencils!

Family

The Blake Family at Felixstowe, circa 1953

From left to right as seen by the camera: (back row) Gordon, Peter, Roger: (centre) Bob, Molly: (front) David and Paddy.

Youngest in the Family
David Blake

There are problems with being the youngest,

especially the youngest of seven.

One headache –

hand-me-downs.

Most of my clothes had already been worn by Gordon

   by Peter

    by Roger

     by Bob

       luckily not too often by Molly

        but definitely by Paddy.

I was the only one in the infants who

had a shirt with a 16 inch collar and 40 inch chest

   (sleeves rolled up 64 times).

I was the only one in the infants who

wore adult trousers, as wide at the waist as a clown's

(turn-ups chafing armpits).

I was the only one in the infants who

wore a National Service, RAF flying jacket,

sheepskin-lined for added summer warmth

(goggles left in the cloakroom).

Mum insisted wearing hand-me-downs wouldn't do me any
harm.

Now though

I suffer from almsacophobia,

an aversion to charity bags.

And they are in season at the moment.

Daily they drop, unwelcomed, onto my mat.

Whatever the cause,

their pleading heart requests for old clothing

I cast off

in a not-a-good-fit

of pique.

Such a shoddy response

will surely cost me dear

come my own great collection day

when I'll stand on the pavement near the pearly gates

(some time between the hours of 7.30 a.m. and 5.30 p.m.)

waiting to be sorted by Saint Peter.

That's all I want to say about hand-me-downs.

If you think there's anything interesting in this

please pass it on to someone else.

The Visit
David Blake

Tug-handed
drag-footed walk
with elder brother,
the weekly visit to gran's.
We always called it gran's
though step-grandad too would be there.

Through the street-gate to the side door,
hoping he was still at his beloved allotment,
hoping no muddy boots were there waiting to be scraped,
hoping for no whiskery presence in the cottage.

The door gaped open on the instant of our knock
and gran eagerly welcomed us into the fusty interior
where he would be sitting,
unkempt,
unshaven,
with spittle-ended pipe,
ready to do his duty
as we were doing ours.

We were ushered to the front room,
uneven slabs and low ceilings conspiring to shrink me.

Stooped gran would place
on the lace cloth of the table
the weekly treats –
glasses containing a thimbleful of Tizer
and a Mars Bar.
Just one Mars Bar.

He would cough with the effort of rising,
splutter the two paces to the table, and proceed,
with all the ceremony of a master carver at a banquet,
to
slice
one
sliver
of
Mars
Bar
for
each
of
us.

How sweet
the fleeting, melt-in-mouth moment
but oh!
how great the cost.

Sir Percy Blake
David Blake

If it wasn't for the unfortunate incident I'm going to relate, one of my ancestors would have been 250 years old this year.

Sir Percy Blake lived in Dover and he had ferries at the bottom of his garden. He was not the brightest. Some people in the Dover area said he was a sandwich short of a picnic and the smart arses there said he was a Sandwich short of a set of Cinque Ports.

Sir Percy Blake managed to get himself involved in the French Revolution and it all began when he misunderstood some news he heard in town.

He thought that a sweet factory had been attacked – the Storming of the Pastilles. He later found out, in fact, that it occurred on July 14th 1789 and it was to do with the release from prison of...er...seven men. Obviously, an event worthy of a national holiday.

Further news reached Sir Percy, of hundreds of aristocrats being executed, and he determined to do his best to save as many as possible and smuggle them to England.

He initially tried to garner support from his friend Sydney Carton but he said he had a far, far better thing to do. So Sir Percy decided to work alone, surviving on his wits. Bad move that. He convinced himself he was a master of disguise and subterfuge. Bad move that.

He crossed the English Channel and attempted many rescues but none of them worked, due to his incompetence. However, after each of his exploits, he would leave at the scene his calling card, a piece of paper on which was coloured a red spot. Because of this, Sir Percy Blake became known as The Scarlet Pimple.

But things came to a head.

Each time he crossed to France, he was determined to try out the fast food meals for which France was, and still is, renowned.

Each channel port had its own speciality - Dieppe pan pizzas, Boulogne in the bag rice, Dunkirk doughnuts and the famous Bayeux tapas. On this fateful day, he decided to try the burgers of Calais.

He went into a branch of Burger No King. His French was usually im-pecc-ab-ler but on this day he got confused when ordering "A whopper and please hold my gherkins." Things got worse when he tried to mime it.

There was confusion in the shop and the door flew open and a strong wind removed his hat and wig. His cover was blown. Under the hat was a false passport. Unfortunately, it was for The Scarlet Pimple from Acne in London.

The customers all shouted, "Le Scarlet Pimple! Zit alors!"

He was arrested for taking libertés with the Revolutionary Government and was transported to Paris. There he was thrown into a small cell, very, very temporary accommodation for crestfallen aristocrats, seventy two of them at the last comte. Sir Percy was just one face in the cowed.

He missed out on getting the final piece of bedding. That was the last straw. He was never at his best when his back was against the wall and spent a very restless night. Thoughts of his home town repeated over and over and over in his mind.

The next morning the guards pinned up a list of those being transported to the guillotine and unfortunately, he was a starter on the a la cart menu. He was manhandled with other prisoners. He hated this rough and tumbrel and he was surprised by the hostile environment created by the noisy jeers from the crowds lining the streets as they went down Equalite Street and Rue D'Awakening. They crossed the final bridge over the Seine and Sir Percy realised he had reached the Pont of No Return.

Such had been the popularity of killing aristocrats that the revolutionaries had had to outsource the executions. Despite the huge number of cuts, the leading firm, De Capita, was doing very well indeed.

59

A very large crowd had gathered to watch. In the best seats were women sarcastically knitting hats and scarves for aristocrats and Sir Percy was aware of the clacking of their needles and their tongues.

He was the first to be led towards the guillotine, to loud jeers from the spectators. Sir Percy was placed head down on a wooden block within the huge contraption. He found the weave of the basket beneath him very attractive and the French craftsmanship surprisingly pleasing. They had also stained some of it red, no doubt getting the dye by crushing cochineal beetles.

"Maintenant!" shouted the executioner.

Sir Percy expected the worst, but nothing happened. The blade had refused to drop. He was ordered to stand up while things were checked. There was a great deal of grumbling and heckling from the crowd.

A couple of minutes later, Sir Percy was back in position, another shout of "Maintenant!" and again nothing happened. Many spectators decided to pack up their knitting and "head off" elsewhere.

There was real confusion and arguments going on amongst the work force. The remaining members of the public were shouting at the executioner, who was badly affected. He started to believe everyone was picking on him – he was suffering from a Percy-execution complex.

Sir Percy was extremely curious about the design of the guillotine and had a close examination of it. Looking up, he said, "I think I can see what the problem is."

He pointed upwards.

"There's a small wedge of wood jammed in the mechanism near the blade. Clear that and it's bound to work."

It did.

It worked very well.

Thus ended the story of Sir Percy Blake, The Scarlet Pimple.

He is not remembered by many beyond serious scholars of the French Revolution and flippant members of the Blake family.

However the manner of his demise has been passed down over the years, although usually ascribed to a person other than he.

Telephone Calls with a Relative Stranger
Susan Hermann

The call came out of the blue. I was in the kitchen cleaning up after our evening meal when the telephone rang. I picked up the handset and you know how it is when you are busy, you wedge the phone between your ear and shoulder and carry on with what you are doing. I was expecting to speak to one of the boys, as calls in the evening were usually from one of our two sons.

"Hiya."

"Susan, is that you?"

Not one of the boys then!

"Hi yes, this is Susan. It's a dreadful line, very faint. Who's calling?"

"Susan, it's your father."

At this point the phone became dislodged from its precarious position between my head and shoulder and fell to the floor. I hastily retrieved it with my wet, soapy hands.

"Sorry about that I dropped the phone. Are you still there?"

"Er – yes, Susan, I can hear you fine."

"Who did you say it was?"

"Suze - it's Dad."

"Ah – mm - I'm very sorry, you have the wrong number!"

"Are you sure? You said 'yes – it is Susan'!"

"Look, I'm sorry, I know it's a coincidence but you definitely have the wrong number."

"Wait – er – Susan, don't go! I think you tried to contact me recently ... please...wait."

I put the phone down hurriedly and stood looking at it for a second. How weird was that?

My husband Mike wandered through into the kitchen after the call. "Who was on the phone? You look quite perplexed."

"It was a wrong number," I said quite abruptly.

Mike looked at me with that quizzical expression I know so well; I see this expression on his face quite often when I'm being vague or silly. He waited for me to continue.

"He said he was my father."

"Ahah - no wonder you are scrubbing those pans so vigorously!" he teased.

"Yeah, it threw me a bit. I didn't quite know what to say to him. Still it was only a wrong number, he's probably chatting happily with his daughter Susan right now! "

"Was there a number on the call display?" my husband asked, with that amused twinkle in his eyes.

"Don't be daft," I said. "The number was shown as withheld."

"Of course it was," he laughed. "Are you sure you're okay, 'cos those pans are spotless now? They've never been so clean!"

"Yup, I'm fine," I responded, pretending to throw one of the pans at him. Mike can always make me laugh, even when I'm snappy with him!

That night in bed I couldn't settle, recalling the brief conversation on the phone, thinking how good it would have been to really talk to Dad. I had lots to tell him, but after twenty-five years I wouldn't know where to start.

Eventually I slept but it was a restless, troubled sleep, full of shadows and 'what ifs'.

The next morning the shadows were gone and I felt annoyed with myself that I had allowed a wrong number to affect me... Good Lord, losing sleep over a misdialled call, how ridiculous was that?

Later the following morning the telephone rang again.

"Hello."

"Er – Susan - it's me again."

"Look I'm so sorry, you have rung the wrong Susan again."

I pondered why is it that **we** apologise for not being the person the caller wants to speak to, after all, **they** made the mistake in the first place!

"Have I? It's these new-fangled phones, the buttons are so small I can't see the numbers very well."

"Did you manage to get hold of your daughter last night?"

"Yes but she couldn't stay on the phone for very long. She seemed quite surprised that I'd called her."

"Oh well, it was good that you were able to reach her."

"Yes it was. Well, I'm sorry to have bothered you again."

"No problem. Bye."

Poor old fella, I thought, he sounded quite elderly and confused. Still it blew away the last of the shadows from the previous night. He is definitely ringing the wrong number. If he rings again I'm going to have to find out what number he is trying to reach, as it must be very similar to ours.

A few days later the telephone rang again. It was during the day when my husband was at work.

"Hello."

"Ah, I think I've got the wrong Susan again!"

"Yes you have. I'm often wrong but I've never been the 'wrong' Susan before!"

"Forgive me, I'm being a pest, aren't I? I still don't know what I'm doing wrong with this phone. It was so much easier years ago when you had to dial the numbers."

"Oh yes," I laughed, "I remember those phones; they were big and heavy and you certainly couldn't carry them around like the mobile phones of today. What number are you trying to reach for your daughter?"

He told me the number he had been trying to call and it was the same as ours, except for the dialling code which was one number different. He was pressing the six on the keypad instead of the nine, close to it.

"Do you ring your daughter every day?"

"No, I haven't spoken to her much until recently."

"Don't you keep in close contact with her?"

"We used to be very close. We would talk about anything and everything, but we have been separated for many years. I've caught sight of her from time to time. She seems very happy and she always seems to be laughing."

"Did you have a falling-out? Is that why you don't see each other?"

"Oh no, nothing like that! I had to leave my family. I didn't want to but I had no choice in the matter. It was quite distressing."

A thought occurred to me when he said this that he might have been in prison, so thought it best not to pursue the matter.

"Is there any way you can meet up again, especially as you do see her occasionally?"

"I had a lovely wife and family, three daughters and a son, but now I am only able to speak to my daughter Susan and I have to be careful what I say to her or she may stop taking my calls."

"That's a shame. One thing is puzzling me though – when you called me the first time you said that your daughter had tried to contact you recently. Why then was she surprised that you had rung her?"

"I think it was because it was unexpected after so many years. I knew she had had some brilliant family news recently and had sent a message to tell me. I just wanted her to know that I shared her happiness."

"Well perhaps now you have made contact with her, it will be a new start for you both. I do hope it works out for you."

"I hope so too. Can I call you again?"

"Well you have my number but it's best if you speak to the 'right' Susan, isn't it?"

"Thanks then, bye."

After the third call I felt concern for the poor man as he sounded so elderly and lonely. How awful to be estranged from his family in the latter years when you do need your family around you. Of course, I didn't know the circumstances of his family break-up, but if he had been in prison for a long time it would have had to be for something very serious. Perhaps his family didn't want anything more to do with him and couldn't forgive him.

For some reason I didn't tell Mike about the other calls. He would have only teased me about finding another 'worthy cause' to care about and after all, it was only a few phone calls. Anyway, I thought, 'the old fella' probably wouldn't ring again now that he knew what he was doing wrong with the phone.

A couple of weeks passed and from time to time I thought about 'the old fella', but as there had been no further calls I assumed things were improving in his life so that he didn't need to talk to a stranger. Funnily though, around about this time, Mike started getting quite exasperated with the telephone; so many wrong numbers, he was getting quite cross. I had just come in and I heard him shouting into the phone saying, "Please don't ring this number again, you are becoming a pest. If you ring again I'll get BT to put a trace on you!"

"Problem?" I said.

"These people," he said, "you would think that when they dialled the wrong number they would have the courtesy to say so instead of just leaving me talking to thin air. They don't even hang up – it is very annoying."

"It's probably my lover," I joked.

"I thought of that," he said, "but then I thought you probably didn't have much time to devote to a lover at the moment!"

"That's true," I said wearily, "neither the time nor the energy. In fact, at the moment I'm not much of a wife either, so shall we get take-away again for tea? I haven't had time to shop again."

"Indian, Chinese, Thai or pizza?" he asked.

The next call came from the 'old fella' just as I was going out to see my mum.

"Hello."

"Susan, it's me. Are you busy?"

"Hi, how are you? I have been wondering how you were getting along. I was just going out to see my mum but I have a few minutes to talk."

"Oh, good. Is your mum well?"

"Mmm, not too good. She is in a nursing home near here. Some days she knows me, on other days she doesn't, that's part of her Alzheimer's. We go from day to day really."

"That must be distressing for you. Do you have any family that can help you with supporting her?"

"I have two sisters and a brother but they all live abroad; both my sisters are in America and my brother is in Australia. We speak frequently but, by necessity, the responsibility for day to day care of Mum is with me."

The line went a bit muffled at this point, but I felt sure he said something like "Aah, that explains it."

"Hello, are you still there? The line went a bit fuzzy for a moment."

"I asked how long your mum has been ill," he said.

"About four years really, although the condition has been much worse recently. I used to get upset about it but as long as she is well cared for and safe, that is all I can do for her. Anyway, how are you? Have you been talking to your daughter some more?"

"Not recently, I haven't been able to get through, but I did try to trace my wife. I went to where we used to live but she'd moved on a long time ago and there was no way of finding her."

"I am sure your daughter may tell you if you ask her, but you'll probably have to approach it very gently, your family may not be ready."

I wondered 'why oh why' was I getting involved; I'm no counsellor and I'm probably saying all the wrong things!!

"Oh, I will be careful. Well, I won't keep you from your mum. I hope you find her well."

"Okay then, bye."

Mum was having a really good day. She didn't know who I was but as I sat and gently talked to her she kept smiling at something I was saying. Well, not exactly smiling, more beaming! I had taken some pictures of my new grand-daughter for her to see so I hoped that somewhere in her scrambled thought processes, her great grandchild had made a special connection.

It was a really good visit. She was happy and settled today so I took the opportunity to do some food shopping after I left. Mum's health was so precarious that even taking time out to do some shopping was a risk at that time. I could be called back to the nursing home at any moment. Thank goodness for mobile phones! Mike would be pleased; tonight we could have a break from take-out food.

When I returned home the phone was ringing and I managed to get to it before the answer phone kicked in.

"Hello."

"I've got some really good news!"

"Hi, two calls in one day, my goodness! You sound very excited, tell me your news."

"I've found her! I'm afraid I was a bit deceitful though. I followed my daughter and she led me to my wife and it was really good to see her."

"My goodness, I bet that was a huge surprise for your wife. Was your daughter cross with you because you followed her?"

"Ah – er - my daughter didn't know and I waited until she had left before I talked to my wife."

Oh dear, I thought, this is going badly wrong already.

"Did your wife know you after so many years? Was she pleased to see you?"

"Of course she did. The girl and young woman I knew are still there in her eyes. She may be old like me, but as soul mates we are still young!"

"Won't your wife tell your daughter that you have visited her?"

"No, I don't think so – er - sometimes even ageing parents keep secrets from their children!"

"I hope you two aren't planning to elope!" I joked. "Is your wife in good health?"

"She's been quite poorly but she will improve. I may not be able to ring you much over the next few days as I am going to try to keep her company for a while -we've a lot of catching up to do. I just wanted to let you know."

"Okay, take care, and let me know how you are doing some time."

"Okay, I'll try."

Somehow I thought I would not be hearing from 'the old fella' again and once his family found out that he had deceived them there would be a further breakdown in relations. Was this my problem though? No, I had enough to do caring for Mum.

The next few weeks were very hard. Mum's condition deteriorated and we had to accept that she was slipping away. During this time there were no signs that she was aware of anything, except on the night she died she squeezed my hand and smiled again. In the end, it was as peaceful as it could be under the circumstances.

Of course, the following days were busy taken up with making the necessary arrangements and co-ordinating the date of the funeral with my sisters' and brother's travel arrangements to attend. After Mum's funeral we all went back to our house. The answer phone indicated one new message and as I walked through the hallway I pressed to action the message replay.

"Hello Suze, it's me again. I just wanted to ring you to let you know that everything is OK, my darling wife is with me again. She was a bit tired after the journey but she will be fine. I won't be able to ring you again but just wanted to say thanks for everything, from both of us. Oh, and apologise to your husband for me. I didn't mean to be a pest, I just couldn't get him to hear what I was saying. Bye."

Mike turned to me and said, "Was that the guy who rang before, a few weeks ago?"

"Your wrong number explained!" I said. Well, I wasn't about to tell Mike that I had been talking to the guy quite frequently over the past few weeks, was I? Especially as by then I was convinced he was a lifer on parole.

As I pressed the erase button for the message I heard an exclamation from Annie who was behind me. I turned to my elder sister who had followed me into the hall. She stood, shocked, staring at the answer machine. She was as white as a sheet.

"What's the matter Annie? Are you okay?"

"Christ, Su, that sounded just like Dad; he was the only one who ever called you 'Suze.'"

Mike looked first at me and then at Annie and said, "C'mon you two, don't be daft. Your dad died twenty-five years ago, didn't he? I'll put the kettle on. We all need some tea, or even something a bit stronger."

Later I tried to ring the number that I thought was for the 'right' Susan, but, of course, it was unobtainable.

Perhaps, just perhaps, the 'old fella' had been ringing the right number and the 'right' Susan all along!

Memories

Violet Blake, the mother of David, Newlands, Brixworth, 1926

Childhood Street
Paul Palmer

When Sunday roast aromas
filled our neighbourhood street,
there was no sound of running or skipping,
from our childhood feet.

We could not wear old play clothes,
go fishing for tiddlers in the brook.
So we stuck brightly coloured stamps
into our Sunday School books.

For calmness dwelt
upon that Sabbath day,
dressed in our Sunday best,
not allowed to run outside and play.

After Sunday dinner
we would build with Meccano,
do a puzzle or a craft.
If we became too excited,
Dad would say, 'Don't act so daft!'

Sunday tea was meat or fish paste
and to fill up your belly
there was more bread and butter
with tinned fruit and jelly.

Round the open fire,
sitting in the kitchen,
weekday tea was bread and jam
and sometimes bread and dripping.

Painted cricket wickets
 upon an old brick wall.
Or two woolly sweaters,
goal posts to catch the ball.

Those games we played,
there was none better.
Game over,
pull back on, that holey, woolly sweater.

To run and play, build dens,
picnic across the fields and the rec.
And to make pea shooters,
from the stems of keck.

With its smells of tobacco
and newspaper print,
into the corner shop
we would sprint.

For penny chews,
 aniseed balls and liquorice sticks,
lollipops, gob-stoppers,
and sherbet dips.

We carried penknives
and played with matches,
climbed trees with grazed knees,
collecting scabs, cuts and scratches.

Yet our childhood
could have been no better.
Girls tied ropes to gas lamp posts
and skipped to 'Salt, mustard, vinegar, pepper.'

Saturday morning minors,
we called the pictures or the flicks.
Cheering at Flash Gordon's sparklers,
out of a cardboard rocket ship.

Scrumping apples and cherry knocking,
sword fighting with a stick.
Kiss chase, hide and seek, leap frog,
or playing a game of tick.

On those same streets,
making boots and shoes, factories dwelt.
Producing nuts and bolts, iron and steel,
they did cast, weld and smelt.

Workers with sandwiches and flasks,
in gas mask bags,
the swishing of bicycle spokes.
Demob suits loosely hung
on thin, pale working blokes.

The factory chimneys,
smoking tall,
The wailing sirens, redundant from war,
but to beckon to work, their eerie call.

Trilbys, caps and bowler hats,
all men for ladies they would doff.
From schoolboys and working men,
to bank managers and the toff.

We listened to Paul Temple on the wireless,
Dick Barton, Jet Morgan and Dan Dare.
We would read our Beanos and Dandys,
under the table or on the stair.

They were swapped and bartered,
but never sold,
for American comics,
were just like gold.

Indians whooped, marbles rolled
and cowboys fired cap guns with glee.
Fights broke out over cigarette cards
and once a champion conker belonged to me.

Outside, hop-scotch, chalked on hot summer path.
Dissolved, distorted, streaked by rain.
In the classroom, teachers strict
and stern, but fair,
backed up with a sturdy cane.

In the corner
the teacher made us stand
when caught in class,
propelling paper pellets from a rubber band.

Throwing snowballs in the playground,
sucking icicles and making a slide.
With hot aches in our hands,
when we went back inside.

Parents clipped us round the ear
and sent us all to bed,
when we were found playing doctors and nurses
in our dad's old garden shed.

Boys would snigger
and snicker
at the sight
of girls in navy knickers.

As girls tossed
against a wall,
some modestly tucked in their skirts,
while others just let them fall.

Now Mr Wolf has run out of time,
Queenie has no longer got the ball.
Hide and seek is now replete,
see we haven't, no not at all.

Yet still I smell
the Sunday roasting meat,
hear the shouts and echoing cries
of our old childhood street.

Now those kids have grown and flown
to all parts of the globe.
But still its pitted tarmac and old kerbstones
cling to its timeless road.

Paul Palmer, 1964

Day Trips
David Blake

I didn't have anything that could be classed as a holiday until I was about twelve. Instead I went out on day trips, on a coach, these being organised by my mum. Every year, and sometimes twice a year, she would book a coach from a firm based in Kingsthorpe and request the same driver, Pat Perryman, whose lively personality and helpfulness added so much to the occasion. Mum would fill about half the coach with family members, then book in village friends, and finally advertise any remaining seats by placing a card in the window of Mayes' newsagents. To my memory there was never a spare seat. Given the cramped nature of the vehicle, a bit of space would have come in very handy, especially on long homeward journeys. Mum would keep meticulous lists and collect deposits, with everyone settling up the full payment just before the big day.

To make good use of the day an early start was essential, usually at about 5.30 or 6. The coach would be parked in front of what were then the Council Offices in Spratton Road, Brixworth and often most people had congregated before its arrival, laden down with packed lunches and enough clothing to counteract whatever the weather was liable to throw at us.

Destinations included London Zoo, Portsmouth Naval Dockyard and the beautiful Wye Valley but by far the most regular and popular was the seaside resort of Great Yarmouth. Roads to the East Coast were very different in those days, with less direct routes and less dual carriageways so journey times were probably about an hour and a half longer than nowadays. Regular toilet and leg-stretching stops were planned and I was always fascinated by the early morning activity around the horseracing town of Newmarket. I still recall standing alongside the coach as a group of thoroughbred racehorses appeared through the swirling mist on a nearby gallop; a magical moment at a time of the day I'd have normally been asleep.

My many visits mean Yarmouth itself is a blur of memories. We weren't ones for much time sitting on the beach – that tended to be done whilst waiting for coach pick-up time, not as sun and sand worshippers. This was no time to relax! Rather, there would be a quick paddle in a usually bitter North Sea before the South Denes amusement park was invaded, where the most exciting rides of roller coaster, ghost train and dodgems shouted out to us to spend most of our pocket money. Careful tactics were required if any coins were to last until afternoon, and these were usually pennies soon to be swallowed up by arcade games.

There were walks on the piers and the long promenade, a builder of appetites before the inevitable meal. Whatever had previously been devoured during packed breakfast or lunch times, the day was not complete without fish and chips, cod or haddock fresh in a fishing port, so different in flavour to when it had journeyed over a hundred miles inland to our local chip shops. Greasy mouthed, we could still manage to wolf down an ice cream for afters.

In those times, not many people had a camera but there were always some people willing to snap away – locals in the employ of a company called Barkers who wandered the promenade, piers and amusement parks, clicking and then informing those captured that the photographs would be ready to view near Wellington Pier by four o'clock. And they were, hundreds of them displayed on boards and surrounded by huddles of day trippers or those on longer vacations in the caravan parks or bed and breakfasts. Lots of our party purchased their personal visual memento of the day, one that was placed in a small cardboard folder emblazoned with 'Barkers'.

Many exhausted travellers got to the coach collection point before the allocated time, with the early start and long walks in hot conditions affecting even the fittest in the party. The drive home was a long one and I remember my dad making an admiral's hat out of folded newspaper, in an effort to interest me and keep me awake.

However, there was one more treat in store, the pub stop in St Neots. It was about an hour from home and a welcome break for all concerned. The Bridge House was alongside the River Great Ouse and lit by chains of fairy lights which reflected in the water, creating a wonderful atmosphere. Children weren't allowed into the main bars but there was a section where we could sit safely, away from the river. Our special treats – bottles of cherryade and packets of cheese crisps, the latter of which were then available only in pubs - were delivered by adults desperate to quench their own thirsts.

We would feel part of this ceremonial homecoming near the borders of Northamptonshire and afterwards voices on the coach were raised once more to morning level and beyond, with rendition of songs including, of course, "Oh! We Do Like To Be Beside The Seaside", as we closed in on Brixworth. The singing was always led by my two oldest brothers, Gordon and Pete, the former who could sing very loudly, the latter who could sing in tune.

Sometime after midnight, passengers spilled off the coach near the Council Offices, thanking and tipping the driver for his part in a successful enterprise, and wended their way home.

Mum, too, got her rightful share of praise. After all, if it wasn't for her, many of us would not have travelled very far from our home village from one year to the next.

Cut the Crap
Michael Hermann

Here we are in the early 1980s and it seems to me that some people are not too fussed about where their dogs roam to empty their bowels. Some folk simply let out their animals from their homes and wait for them to return a few pounds lighter. This means that our footpaths and various other public areas are becoming fouled with unhealthy dog faeces. This includes the front lawn to our bungalow which is 'open plan'. For some time, some of the dogs in the village have been able to regularly deposit their poo liberally and without hindrance on their favourite parts of our territory. I have discovered that it is impossible to deter these unwelcome visitors from returning on a daily basis to seek out their specially chosen toileting areas.

I always cut our grass with an ancient but effective Flymo hover mower. It has, however, been necessary for me to devise a 'pre-cut' strategy for this activity and this always takes the form of a quick survey for stones, litter and other debris that appear from time to time, but also, of course, to spot the piles of dog poo.

The offensive smelly turds are dealt with by my using a bricklayer's trowel and a small shovel! As I work in Northampton for five days during the week, there will always be several days' worth of these unsightly heaps on the lawn, in differing stages of decomposition. The easiest ones to deal with are the older, whitish ones, which I can flick easily onto the shovel. The more recent ones though are more problematic. Once cleared, the weekly deposits can be carried across the road and deposited under a hedge which borders the roadside field.

Being an academic by profession, I believe that some serious research into this problem can be justified. Although cynically I sometimes wonder if research is just a means of examining some process which works well in practice, then constructing a model to see if it actually works in theory, I decide that I must really attempt to do some analysis of my own to try to put paid to the canine activities which are souring my weekly mowing activities.

Weekend observations come first and I become obsessed with peering down the road, watching out for the doggy culprits. My regular depositors can be spotted miles away, staggering, bowels bulging, heading in a determined and unfettered manner towards our home. Their long, wet, dangling tongues seem to give the impression of overt, happy anticipation. As they get closer they actually seem to be grinning and my presence during their toileting does not appear to impede them. Not only that, I notice that once the evacuation process has started, there appears to be no way to end it prematurely, nor is there a humane way in which I can intervene to physically reverse the process.

So how about directly confronting the dog owners?

Early one Sunday morning, peering through my bedroom window at the front of our bungalow, I spot one of my regular unleashed offenders fouling the grass. This time though its unconcerned owner is actually present, dangling a redundant dog lead, oblivious to my appearance at the nearby window. I decide to attempt a mature and rational conversation with the offending pet owner. Instead I open the window and yell at him! "Why do you let your animal do that on my lawn?"

Although I am not religious, I am a devout coward and this was a very unusual action on my part. The response, though, is unhelpful.

"What's it got to do with you? Who the hell do you think you are anyway? This grass belongs to the council."

Technically he is wrong; according to our land deeds we, together with nearby neighbours, own the land up the centre of the road which passes our properties. I don't bother to enlighten him.

"I'm the person who has to clear up the mess," I whine.

My protestations fall on deaf ears and the chap and his dog move on for today. But they will be back tomorrow for sure.

Failure! But later that morning as I am preparing to cut the same piece of grass, I get a second chance to test my bravery and confrontation theory when I see Nick approaching with his large, unleashed, black hound. The beast is heading for my patch. Now I have a friendly relationship with Nick and as his animal prepares to do its worst, I decide that, for the second time today, some positive action on my part is most certainly required.

But I swiftly exit, out of sight, to the rear of the bungalow, to do some unnecessary tidying up.

There I remain for several minutes until the inevitable has ended and Nick and his empty dog have disappeared from view.

Despite this second abject failure, my research has also provided me with another strategy, aimed not at the owners but directly at the animals. It is designed to discourage them from using their regular haunts on our lawn for their daily ablutions. So how might this work?

Once the lawn has been cut, it is hosed down. After this, I treat it with a substantial amount of a special but very expensive substance called 'Dogsoff'. This, I have been reliably informed, will deter even the most persistent of animals from approaching their toilets in our garden.

I adopt this technique for a few weeks, hoping for a significant return on investment.

If anything, though, the problem becomes worse. It appears that the wretched dogs are getting hooked on the substance and, what's more, the word seems to be spreading.

But now, as often happens to me, fate takes a hand. It is Saturday morning, in the middle of my 'Dogsoff' routine, when my next-door neighbour and great friend Kish appears in front of me. He demands, in his deep, booming voice, to know what I am doing.

Now I've known Kish for years and he knows that I call him 'Mr Theory'. He is a self-confessed instant expert on every subject under the sun. He has an MPhil in the glaringly obvious and also a PhD in hindsight. Over the years we have insulted each other overtly with great enjoyment, but our friendship has never wavered. It is important, however, to understand one important aspect of Kish's behaviour; once his advice has been given, he never hangs around to see if it ever comes to practical fruition!

"No, no, no! Waste of money that 'Dogsoff' stuff. Get some Madras curry and chilli. That's what you need. Grind it all together to form a fine powder and then spread it all over the grass. One sniff of that and those dogs will never return."

"What a joke, "I think to myself, "I'm going to forget that daft idea."

By now it is raining and I can't finish my lawn cutting.

The next day, Sunday morning, unbelievably, I find myself adopting Kish's crazy suggestion as a last-ditch attempt to resolve my dog turd problem. Having prepared my concoction of 'Tesco strongest Madras' mixed with chilli powder, I find myself liberally sprinkling it on the 'hot spots' on the front lawn. I have this vision of sneezing, howling pooches, missions unaccomplished, hot-footing it back to their homes, never to return.

But then the unexpected happens. A sharp breeze blows most of the remaining powder from its container directly into my face.

I start sneezing and coughing and have tears pouring down my face. Passing motorists are well entertained today, for free, by the sight of a balding, pot-bellied, red-faced demon, leaping around in the garden shouting "Never again, never ever again!" As usual, Kish is nowhere to be seen. I return to the bungalow to wash my face and to try to recover my dignity.

Later, as I still have to mow the lawn properly, I start up the ageing Flymo and start to manoeuvre it across the grass.

Hang on! Just a minute! Something seems wrong. I am now sensing an aroma of curry, mingling with another much more sinister pong. It takes me a nano-second to realise that I have just located the Flymo directly above a large pile of newly laid 'you-know-what' that had evaded my pre-cut audit! The centrifugal force of my powerful mower has also spread the miniscule, smelly globules indiscriminately over a five-metre radius, the epicentre of which is, of course, yours truly.

I am now totally smothered in my own obsession!

Later, my long-suffering wife Su tells me that there are lots of open-plan gardens in Australia, but there they have a different plan to solve their doggy-do dilemma. Her story is incredulous, it's a wind-up, I'm sure! A half-empty lemonade bottle placed in the middle of the lawn?

What nonsense! It could never work here! Or could it?

I rush off to our kitchen to find a lemonade bottle.

Places

Delapre Abbey, Northampton, with a horse jump in the foreground

Delapre Abbey, Northampton
David Blake

Key Events in the History of Delapre Abbey

Delapre Abbey, on the southern edge of Northampton, was the site of a nunnery which was founded in about 1145 A.D. by the second Simon de Senlis, Earl of Northampton. The first Earl had built Northampton Castle and founded the priory of St Andrew, which was named after nearby St Andrew's Road. The nunnery was called St Mary de la Pre, which translates as St Mary of the Meadow. There were many advantages to the site – proximity to the River Nene, to designated land near Hardingstone, to Yardley Chase where the nunnery was granted a cartful of wood every day but the clincher was it was only an eight minute walk to 'The Giggling Sausage' café.

The order by which both the priory and the nunnery was ruled was part of the Benedictines, specifically called the Cluniac order. This was named after the town of Cluny in Burgundy. Probably their most famous citizen was Georges de Cluny.

Two events of national importance occurred at Delapre. In 1290 the funeral cortege of Queen Eleanor, wife of Edward I, halted here overnight. In life, she was a forthright person and you wouldn't have wanted to make Queen Eleanor cross.

On July 10th 1460, the Battle of Northampton took place near the abbey, fought between Lancastrians and Yorkists. The battle was part of The War of the Roses. A Welsh general commanded the Lancastrian Red Rose troops - Aphid of Monmouth - and the White Rose army was led Richard Neville, Earl of Warwick, who was known as Warwick the Kingmaker. (I think if I'd have been alive in such war-torn days, I'd have been known as David the Peace Taker.)

No monk from St Andrew's attended the battle – they had a prior engagement – but some nuns did venture out to watch. After only 15 minutes of fighting, the casualty figures for civilians and military stood at one nun dead and eighty.

The Yorkists were ultimately successful and King Henry VI was captured, but only Part One. Parts Two and Three had stayed in Stratford-Upon-Avon.

The nunnery at Delapre was closed as part of the wholesale dissolution of monasteries, priories, convents and friaries ordered by King Henry VIII. It was due to be in 1536 but a stay was put on the closure, leading to the nuns chanting "If you're abbey and you know it, clap your hands."

However, the king's chief adviser, Sir Thomas Cummings, encouraged Henry to "get dissolution done," saying it would pass any hindsight test. So, the abbey closed in 1538 and the nuns departed the site. Most stayed true to their calling but some left the order. For them, when the doors of the nunnery slammed shut for the final time, their world ended with a bang, but not a wimple.

Delapre Horse Trials

In the parkland around the abbey there can be seen several horse jumps. This is where the renowned Delapre Horse Trials took place many years ago. When the idea for the event was first mooted there were lots of neigh sayers but after a few successful years, whoa betide any critic. There was sponsorship from Tate and Lyle and the winning rider was awarded the Tate and Lyle Golden Stirrup.

Little did anyone suspect there would also be a different sort of Delapre Horse Trial.

There were two cousins, Bert and Charlie Piggott. The former was from Northampton but the latter was one of the Leicester Piggotts. They took a fancy to riding some of the competition horses housed overnight in the abbey grounds. Even though the building was meant to be secure, the lads found it easy to borrow a couple of mounts and had a bareback ride over parts of the course.

Little did they know that this was the year that equine microchipping had been introduced and thus the horses' movements were being monitored. This tracking was being done in Cheltenham, by the Gee Gee CHQ. The horses' owners and the police were informed. So by dusk the next day, a special surveillance team had been set up by the local cops, in the local copse.

After less than an hour they heard a sound, a rustling noise. Bert and Charlie were riding the horses again. They were quickly arrested and made statements admitting that they had taken the horses and had jumped the stone wall and the oxer. They asked for twelve other fences to be taken into consideration.

They were found guilty and sentenced to 120 hours community service, cleaning out the stable of the Mayor of Northampton. Bert and Charlie's bareback riding led to them being saddled with a criminal record and thus the famous Delapre Horse Trial concluded.

The Northamptonshire Records Office at Delapre Abbey

For many years Delapre Abbey was home to Northamptonshire's records office, the repository of historical documents about the county. However, on its initial move to the abbey the office was put into temporary accommodation. It was shoved into a small space in the rear section, so was not so much a repository as a suppository. Eventually the facility was housed in appropriate rooms and in the days before the internet and social media it was an extremely valuable resource for researchers.

It was in this period that I requested support for a project I was undertaking linked to my family history. I wished to trace my family's coat-of-arms. I was recommended to contact Jeannie Allergy but when I rang I actually got through to a chap called Harold Dree and made an appointment to see him. He was a very welcoming and helpful chap and I passed on to him the little I knew of my family in the Middle Ages.

When I returned in a fortnight, he was able to show me an illustration of my family's coat-of-arms in the early 16th century.

The right-hand side of the shield as I looked at it was blank. He told me not to worry - this was nothing sinister.

There was a scroll at the base of the shield on which was our family motto, in Latin "Semper in aqua calida," which translates as "Always in difficulty".

It was the left-hand side of the shield, the distaff, he called it, that interested him the most but to me it appeared to have little of note on it. However, Harold was enthused.

There was a line of objects – an egg, a helmet with a plume, and another egg. He said it wasn't often you saw an egg and crest sandwich on a coat-of-arms.

He indicated the plume. "These are feathers taken from a hen," he said. "This all relates to a less than glorious event in history, one in which some of your maternal ancestors chose the wrong side."

Readers, you may remember the mystery of the Princes in the Tower, two young members of the royal family who disappeared from the Tower of London in 1483. Their father was Edward IV and mother Elizabeth Woodville, who was born in Northamptonshire, in the village now called Grafton Regis. The twelve-year-old boy was rightfully King Edward V; the nine-year-old was Richard, Duke of York.

They were in the care of their uncle, the Lord Protector, Richard, Duke of Gloucester, later to become King Richard III and even later, a car park attendant in Leicester. Richard died at the

Battle of Bosworth and the Tudor dynasty began in 1485 with Henry VII.

In 1499 someone claimed to be the Duke of York, one of the missing princes. This man was Perkin Warbeck. He was the son of a chicken farmer and had hatched a plot, backed by some powerful people eager to unseat the Tudors.

Perkin garnered support for his cause, rallying people to his flag, which bore the emblem of a plumed helmet above a chicken. Two of my ancestors, Stuart and Kevin Payton, were persuaded to join him.

It was a failed coop. Perkin, who had a tendency to brood, was concerned about his army. Like his standard, it was paltry. Also, Perkin had been affected by a recurring nightmare. In it, he was discovered to be the impostor he was and ended up being chased by a huge bull before being humiliated in battle. Yes, he had to dream the Impostor – bull dream, to fight the unbeatable foe.

It was foul weather for March when his supporters lined up, ready to make their way to London. Warbeck was at the front, then his officers, then the men. Finally, at the rear, was the priest, Parson Snows. It was the usual Perkin order.

However, their mission was not being taken seriously in the country. Perkin Warbeck was not viewed as the real Duke of York, rather a tribute act. The residents and King's army awaited them on the city walls of London.

"Here comes Pecking Warbeak," they jeered, and shouted for him to cluck off.

The authorities had distributed what they saw as appropriate ammunition. Hard boiled eggs were left with the civilians; dippy eggs with soldiers.

When Perkin's men came into free range, they were pelted. Stuart tried to warn his nearest companion by shouting, "Eggs, Benedict," but there were so many missiles and they were hard to ovoid. The retreat was at panic level and men scrambled over each other to reach safety.

Stuart and Kevin got away unharmed but were obviously shell shocked. Embarrassed, they returned to their home village where henceforth they were known as Chicken Stu and Chicken Kev.

Perkin Warbeck was captured by a troop of cavalry led by Colonel Sanders and was never seen again, although rumour has it that his nuggets were found in a bucket.

This ended the event symbolised on my family's coat-of-arms and I felt some pride in the fact that two of my ancestors, however misguided, had yoked themselves to a cause they saw as just.

I thanked Harold for his diligent research and wrote up the findings to share with members of my family. Their thanks were very gratifying but it's not as if I was doing it for a Pulitzer prize!

London
Michael Hermann

At Greenwich station every Thursday
walking through its gloomy subway,
pigeons in their nests I see.
I wonder if they look for me?

At Euston station, blind and black,
a man is waiting by the track.
The train arrives, can he alight,
this man who only knows the night?

I see the punks in Leicester Square,
with torn blue jeans and orange hair.
Without a ring pierced through my nose,
perhaps it's me with funny clothes.

I see the tourists, curious, eyeing
a sleeping drunk – or is he dying?
A siren wails, blue flashing light,
the law arrives to stop a fight.

I smell the chestnuts, roasting, smoking,
see nearby buskers, singing, joking.
Here's a pub – enjoy real ale
and in the back streets, sex for sale.

I hear a preacher thank the Lord,
but see a legless man ignored.
He needs some money, for a drink,
plenty here to make me think.

I see arcades, inviting, bright,
a young boy plays throughout the night.
He's put his money in the slot.
'Time's up mate – that's your lot.'

I see a girl who ran away,
down and out and easy prey.
High on drugs and sleeping rough,
will life in Soho make her tough?

And so in London every Thursday
as I walk the same old roadway,
familiar faces I will see.
I wonder if they look for me?

Activities and Pastimes

Old Man of Coniston (with Su)

Right Place - Wrong Time
David Blake

I haven't entered the London Marathon this year, never have done. But every year when the event comes around, I do get reminded of the time I nearly won a gold medal for cross-country running. It was many years ago but I can still recall the details.

It occurred in 1966, when I was nineteen, at a time when I was at college in a leafy part of Buckinghamshire. It was near the lovely village of Chalfont St Giles, which is in what was known as "the Stockbroker Belt". The majority of residents welcomed students with folded arms. A few miles the other way was Maple Cross, which you may have heard of. It's quite well known for its long stay car park on the M25.

Newland Park College students fell into two categories – those who applied there as it was close to home and the majority, those of us who had failed to get into our first three choices and so were sent there by the clearing house system.

Quite a few of the lads were training to be PE teachers so the sport there was of a good standard. In 1966 the Athletics Club decided to organise a team event, three runners per team, over a course of about two and a quarter miles. The college had two long drives fanning out from the main buildings, one in the direction of Maple Cross, the other towards Chalfont St Giles. So the course involved running up one drive, looping outside the college grounds and then finishing off down the other drive.

Each team was issued with a letter of the alphabet. I think 25 teams entered because when I went to sign in there was no queue. We were designated the letter L. We decided to call ourselves The L for Leather Boys and this is what we had pinned to the front of our t-shirts. On the back we had the slogan "We can't run but we tan hide."

It's fair to say my team of three was not considered one of the favourites to win. Even though I was playing football for the college first team and trained often, I was one of those players whose speed was deceptive – I was even slower than I looked – and I had no stamina. These attributes made me the obvious candidate for lead-off man.

The second member of our team was Jim Eldridge. Jim was very tall and slim and had expended a lot of energy over the years in creating excuses not to do any physical exercise. His shorts were voluminous, his trainers size twelve. Joining his shorts to his trainers were two of the thinnest, whitest legs in England, ones that Spike Milligan would have described as like two pieces of knotted string.

Who could possibly run the anchor leg of such a team? None other than Dick Bezodis, who made up for a distinct lack of skill in all sports by sheer enthusiasm and will-power. Dick would always give 110%, 120%, 200% for the lads. And Dick was the bandiest person I've ever known. He definitely couldn't have stopped a pig in an alley.

So our legs were short, thin and bandy, which sounds like a firm of solicitors. We appeared quite a sight as we limbered up. I did some stretching exercises, Jim warmed up by putting his hands down the front of his shorts, searching for inspiration. Meanwhile, Dick did his version of star jumps, looking like a demented, giant nutcracker.

When the gun sounded, I started quite well, in about twelfth, as we went around some of the college buildings but by the time we reached the Maple Cross drive I had drifted back to twentieth. Half-way down the drive, I was last. And the gap was ever widening.

As the others turned right, out of the college grounds, I was the only one on the drive. Except, that was, for two people not running that day. There was a car parked on the grass verge. Pete Wedgbury was in the driver's seat of his car and Dunc Bibby was leaning against the side. As I came almost alongside the vehicle, the back door on the passenger's side opened. At exactly the same moment, I must have had a blow-out in my trainers because I swerved off the road and fell into the car, onto the floor, in the well in front of the back seats. The car started and moved off, turning right.

Pete and Dunc kept up a commentary as I was driven past the runners to the grass verge at the top of the second drive. Pete parked the car in such a position that I could slide out unnoticed and lie between the car and a hedge. On a signal from Dunc, I stood up and re-joined the runners. I was in sixth place and felt really fresh and full of energy, whereas those around be seemed hot and rather out of breath. I ran well within myself and handed over to Jim in fifth. In the meantime, Pete had driven back to his position at the top of the first drive.

It was sheer bad luck for Jim that by the time he got alongside the car he was surrounded by other runners and so was unable to take advantage of a ride in a Ford Prefect. There was real dismay on his face as he grimaced towards Pete and Dunc. He was committed to run the whole distance, something he had never, ever envisaged doing.

Dick and I were very concerned once it became obvious Pete's car was not going to appear at the end of the finishing straight. Jim trundled over the line in twenty second position, followed only by props from the college's rugby 4th XV. After an extended recovery time, Jim began cursing me and vowing never to wear trainers again.

Dick set off and, unbeknownst to us, in the meantime Pete had repositioned the car nearer to the college buildings, not far from the start.

Jim and I waited at the finish and exchanged knowing glances as Pete's car appeared at the top of the homeward drive just before any runners came into sight. Dick had managed to follow my energy saving example and, knowing him as I did, it would have certainly cut down on his personal emissions.

We were aware of a back door opening and a shape sliding out. Just in time! The leaders appeared almost immediately. It had been a close run thing...well, when I say "run"...

The first runner was, as expected, Jack Singer, the Secretary of the Athletics Club and organiser of the event. Others from the club were close behind. Suddenly a very distinctive figure could be seen sprinting down the tarmac. It was Dick and he was overtaking athlete after athlete.

It dawned on Jim and I at the same time. "Oh no, he's trying to win!"

I moved more quickly than I had done during the race. I ran down the drive towards Dick, waving my arms wildly. I had to intercept him before it was too late. Winning was not part of the plan!

I got to him just as he was moving into third place. His face changed from fierce determination to puzzlement, as I ran towards him. "Dick," I shouted, "slow down. We're not meant to win. DICK, WE'RE NOT MEANT TO WIN!!!"

Realisation hit home and Dick decided to feign injury. In one of the worst pieces of acting ever seen, Dick, with a loud squeal, dramatically pulled a hamstring.

"Oh!" he shouted, "I seem to have pulled my hamstring," clutching the semi-circular curve of his thigh muscle. He limped the final hundred yards and still managed to come fifteenth.

"Sorry, lads," Dick apologised, "I got a bit carried away."

After the race, we sat in the Student Union bar savouring the day's happenings and received plaudits from our mates who had witnessed our sudden appearances from behind the car. Very soon though the door diagonally opposite opened and there entered Jack Singer and other committee members of the Athletic Club. Jack's face was contorted with emotion and not the sort associated with him having won the race. They headed for us and I thought, "We've done the relay, now we're for the high jump."

"You shower!" Jack barked. "You cheating prats! Do you know how much organisation goes into an event like this? Do you? We do everything by the 3A rules."

"I'm in the 2As," chipped in Pete. "For the car."

"See, you just can't stop peeing about, can you? Amateur Athletics Association! And you obviously didn't know we had stop-watches on all the teams." He paused. "So, we could work out every runner's lap time."

He turned to Dick and went nose to nose with him. "Bezodis, you'll have to let me know about your training methods. I was wondering how it is you can limp the last hundred yards and still beat the college record." Dick had finished in the right place but at the wrong time.

How could we respond?

Mea culpa; Jim aculpa; Dick very much aculpa ... and Pete and Dunc aculpa.

It was mutually agreed that we would not enter a team for the next year's event, nor the next. So basically, a two year ban... A two year ban... for a minor technical infringement like ours.

I did once think about competing in the London Marathon but didn't go through with it. The main reason was that I don't know London very well and I wouldn't have known the best place for Pete Wedgbury to park his car.

Marathon – What Marathon?
Michael Hermann

This story's true and you may laugh,
I wrote it for my Osteopath.
Into his room, with head held high,
I looked the doc straight in the eye.

"Can I run my marathon?
With so much pain, will it be on?"
"Behind that screen – get off your kit,
let me see if you are fit.

What's that you say, a little hitch?
Changing clothes gives you the stitch!
Oh my goodness, dearie me!
Flippin' heck, tee hee hee!

Your maker just can't be excused,
he should have had his plans refused!
How do you work, you're quite a wreck?
You've so much wrong below your neck.

Your back is round, the spine too curved,
I've never seen legs so absurd.
The left one's longer than the right,
Your ankles are a sorry sight!

Up on the couch, don't make a sound,
I'll turn your knees the right way round
and point your feet – just like so -
that's the way they're meant to go.

As for the rest, I have to state,
I need to make an estimate.
It could take me all tonight
to cost out how to put you right.

On 9th of May, if you start,
I hope that I'll have played my part,
but my advice - you're such a mess,
give up running – take up chess!"

Jubilee Gardens,
Sunday May 9th 1982
Michael Hermann

My tears in Jubilee Gardens
were the aftermath
of months of doubt and pain.

Cheering crowds had lined the streets
from start to finish.

She was there,
and friends watched at home.

As Westminster Bridge was crossed,
a dream was fulfilled
and pledges were honoured,
but the strength to run could not have been mine alone.

Twenty six miles in less than five hours
were achieved,
for those who matter,
those who care.

Like Rabbits Caught in the Glare of Floodlights
David Blake

It's an unenviable position to be in, playing against the club you've supported all your life. You know that you could beat them, undermining their quest for success, and perhaps even causing the manager to lose his job. True, the Northamptonshire County Youth Cup may not have been Northampton Town Football Club's main target for the 1963/4 season but when the Cobblers' youth team (Under 18s) were drawn in the semi-final against Brixworth Youth (Under 17s), it seemed very important to us in the village team, especially as the game was to be contested under the County Ground's floodlights. We were to play on a Football League club's hallowed turf that had been caressed by the passes of our heroes (and the car tyres of hundreds of cricket fans when the rest of the ground was used for county cricket in the summer months).

The build-up to the game did not go smoothly, three of our best players deciding to maintain their footballing credibility by not appearing in the game, each citing a pre-booked bout of diarrhoea. They feared we would be humiliated. Personally, I don't feel 14-0 was in any way a humiliation.

Firstly, there was a problem with the floodlights. They stayed on.

Secondly, there were problems with future first-teamers Ronnie Walton and Ray Perryman, and with the other twenty or so Cobblers youth-teamers who seemed to be playing against us. To this day, I'm not even sure if their goalkeeper came back out after half-time.

I remember there were a few problems in persuading our third choice goalkeeper to play, and then during the match to stop him using the comb he had stored down one of his socks. I wonder if Patrick "Flan" Kennedy later bored his children with edited highlights from his heroic back-bending in front of five hundred spectators. It has to be said that his main attribute as a goalkeeper was his neat hair.

I was centre half and can actually only remember touching the ball once, making a sliding tackle on Walton to prevent what would have been the all-important fifteenth goal. The crowd rose as one man and by then I think it was.

Still, there were some positives. Our centre forward Dave West was so impressive taking fifteen kick-offs that he was later to play for Northampton Town Colts. Charlie Barham's statuesque performance at full back was sufficient to gain him a Cobblers' directorship about twenty years later, and I did hear some money changed hands in the deal.

It was an experience I wouldn't have missed – to be in the dressing room area, to run out of the tunnel, to play under lights in front of spectators who had actually paid to be in the County Ground, even if they regretted it!

Water-Skiing at Grendon Lakes
Michael Hermann

Water-skiing can be described as a surface water sport where a person is pulled behind a boat at a speed which enables the participant to skim the surface of the water on either one or two skis. The best fitness advice I could find in respect of this activity was that the skier should have adequate upper and lower body strength, muscular endurance and good balance.

So how did I shape up against these characteristics?

On a scale of ten, one being poor and ten being excellent, as a grossly unfit, paunchy, forty five year old, I would probably be fortunate to have achieved a zero!

Even so, for several years I had been trying to summon up the courage to book a water-skiing lesson. My years of indecision became final one sunny July afternoon when I 'bit the bullet' and found myself at Grendon Lakes.

What had I been worrying about?

As the ski boat sped across the lake, it showered a cascade of shimmering water high into the air. The left hand was gripping the tow rope and the right arm was raised aloft in a confident, posing salute. What a thrilling and invigorating way to enjoy such a beautiful day and it was all so very easy.

Out on the water, Tony, the owner of the ski club, was a brilliant performer, whilst I, with a stupid grin on my face and a stomach churning with anxiety, was at last about to try it for myself.

The boat returned to the pontoon and Tony somehow skipped seamlessly from the water to land in a nonchalant and well-practised routine. Mickey, the instructor who was in charge of the boat, moored it securely and I approached him.

"Do you think you could teach me to do that?" I enquired, thinking hopefully that I should have booked beforehand and maybe I will be reprieved and have to come back another day.

"Well, let's see - go and buy a ticket, grab a wetsuit and lifejacket and off we go."

My heart sank but I did as requested and went to change into the wetsuit. This was my first challenge. I had never donned one before and it wasn't easy. I didn't have a clue but, having struggled into the wetsuit, it felt uncomfortably tight around my rotund frame. I emerged hesitantly from the changing room into the sunlight and hobbled slowly towards the pontoon.

"Well, that's a novelty, Mickey," said Tony, grinning and nodding in my direction.

I had put the wetsuit on back to front!

It was agreed by the experts, though, that this did not seem to make any difference, but when I put on the lifejacket I found that my movement was further restricted – in fact, I was as stiff as a board.

I was handed a set of skis and I lurched forward in a robotic fashion and followed Mickey to the pontoon and then into the ski boat. As we pulled swiftly away from the bank, I knew for sure that years of procrastination had now abruptly and irreversibly ended. I had gone beyond the point of no return and, to make matters worse, I noticed that several spectators had emerged from the clubhouse to watch the entertainment.

A little way out from the pontoon, Mickey powered down the boat and it came to a halt. As instructed, I positioned myself on the rear platform of the craft so that I could attempt my second challenge of the day. This was to put on the skis ready for my lesson. I soon realised that this small area of the boat was an inappropriate perch for someone of my size and shape to undertake this task, and the restricted movement caused by the wetsuit and lifejacket meant I found it very difficult to put on the skis. The boat was rocking to and fro, which did not aid my task, but after some puffing and blowing and a considerable degree of embarrassment, I managed, at last, to get the skis onto my feet. By then, my energy had been badly sapped! I am certain that my sickly, forced grin did little else than reinforce the expectations of the onlookers that this was going to be a hilarious episode for all. Except, that is, for me!

The next of my challenges was to leave the safety of the boat and enter the water. This was actually much easier than I had imagined. I plummeted into the lake and immediately disappeared under the murky water. Had there been a guard of honour present, with nautical whistles and a Union Jack, it would have been entirely appropriate for this fiasco.

After a while, I surfaced but my skis were now moving haphazardly in opposite directions beneath me. More worryingly, I found myself being slowly and unavoidably dragged underneath the ski boat. Mickey, realising my plight, dangled a length of rope to save me from oblivion and the evening news. He then guided me towards the beam on the side of the ski boat which is used, instead of a tow rope, for idiot novices like me to learn how to ski. I gripped the bar for dear life while Mickey explained what was going to happen next. He told me to listen very carefully to all his instructions.

I listened, but not carefully enough. With my knees bent against my bulging chest, skis pointing upwards, half out of the water, and my hands gripping the beam, I waited. My arms were locked straight and my face was contorted in a grimace of terror as Mickey accelerated the boat. I then promptly ignored any of the snippets of information I thought I had understood.

Just seconds later, my skis had been wrenched off my feet. I let go of the beam and I was back in the water, gasping for air and bobbing around like a cork. There was an added extra though – several mouthfuls of tepid lake water. What a treat for the onlookers who, by now, must have decided to settle in for the afternoon - and it was all for free!

"Get the skis back on and we'll try again." Mickey, having turned the boat around to rescue me, sounded a tad fed up! He must have wondered what on earth he had let himself in for this afternoon.

This latest instruction though proved impossible for me to carry out whilst in the water. I had two arms, two feet and two skis, but it was impossible for me to coordinate them all whilst my body was rolling from side to side and bobbing up and down in the water. Instead, I had to settle for hauling myself back onto the platform of the boat. Easier said than done - it took me some considerable time, after which I probably looked like a beached whale. By now, twenty minutes of my fifteen-minute lesson had elapsed. A few groans and whinges later and I had managed to reposition the skis onto my feet and I again plunged into, and then under, the water.

Once back in my 'ready' position clinging onto the ski beam, I blissfully ignored Mickey's shouted instructions as the boat moved off again. By some freak of the laws of motion, I was lifted out of the water and I actually found myself skiing. I felt very uncomfortable though and in fact 'hanging on for grim death' seems an appropriate expression to describe my predicament. My body was aching badly but surely I had shown those spectators a thing or two!

I must be honest - I was not enjoying any of this at all. There was no excitement, no exhilaration, no sense of achievement; just intense fatigue and pain. Ten seconds aloft and I knew that I'd already had enough. But we were now approaching the end of the lake and Mickey shouted to me that I should bend my knee as the boat turned around. But I failed to hear which of the two potential limbs I should use. I tried to fathom it for myself – which seemed to be an appropriate term to describe my probable imminent return to the depths.

"No, no, bend the other leg – and watch out for the wake."

I somehow negotiated the turn but the roar of the boat engine masked any further knee-bending or indeed any other helpful instructions for dealing with the 'wake'. This self-inflicted wave caused by the boat was the first of several, each of which must have been at least a metre high. Somehow I stayed above the water, and as we hit each wave a spasm of pain added further discomfort to my inadequate muscles. After what seemed to be an eternity, we were approaching the opposite end of the lake. This would require another turn and dealing with yet more waves!

Absolutely not! There was no way I intended to face all that again.

"Knackered!" I managed to gasp to Mickey. "I can't do any more!"

"You want to go in?"

I nodded furiously! Relief at last! There was no bending of either of my shaking knees as Mickey veered the boat in the direction of the distant pontoon.

Still some way out from the pontoon and Mickey shouted. "Hold on until I tell you to let go. Hang on, hang on, hang..."

By now I was well beyond dealing with such minor cosmetic details. We were in the middle of the lake, miles from the bank and the pontoon, but I just had to let go of the beam.

Under the water I went yet again, surfacing with yet another mouthful of Grendon Lake, as Mickey, with his face registering undisguised disbelief, circled the boat around me. My lifejacket was again doing a great job of keeping me afloat, but as usual, not very stable. It would have been helpful had my skis been wrenched from my feet at this point. But no! Not only were these stupid things difficult to put on but also they would come off when I didn't want them to. Now though, at my moment of greatest need, I found that my feet refused to be parted from them.

Feeling sick and miserable, I was sure my time was up!

After a few aborted attempts, I eventually managed to pull the wretched skis from my feet and to hold them on top of the water in front of me. By kicking my legs up and down, I started to move slowly in the general direction of the pontoon.

When I arrived at the bank I hauled myself up the ladder attached to the pontoon and pulled myself to my feet while Mickey was mooring the boat.

"Surprising how fit you need to be for this," he said, probably as a gesture of consolation, "but you did get out of the water."

I apologised to Mickey for being so useless and staggered towards the changing rooms, my stomach bloated with water. I knew I wanted to vomit but I couldn't even manage that! My fingers and hands were stiff and aching and so the process of getting out of the wetsuit, even with its zip at the front instead of the rear, was a very lengthy and tedious one. I was hoping that a welcome hot shower would improve my morale but it did little to ease my aching muscles. On a positive note, at least this marked the end of my water-skiing experience.

There were a couple of lads in the changing room as I emerged from the shower room and one of them told me that 'the first time is always the worst.' I made a polite response but in reality, I couldn't care less. As far as I was concerned, I had been water-skiing twice – that is, once and never ever again!

It was still a beautiful summer's day when I finally sneaked out of the clubhouse, keen to avoid any of my audience, but I needed a very long rest in the car before setting off for home.

It was as I was driving through the outskirts of Northampton that I thought about entering an 'iron man' competition. But the thought of scorching all those shirts soon changed my mind! I may have lost my dignity today, I thought, but I had at least retained my sense of humour.

It was then that I saw the poster offering an introductory hang-gliding lesson.

Difficult Times

Tourbillon

Cobweb
Michael Hermann

Life is like a cobweb
and we are its architects,
its threads and its guardians.

Our words and deeds vibrate
and trigger actions in others
and it is damaged
by the storms of turmoil.

Yet it is repaired,
painstakingly and patiently
until it is destroyed once again.
And this cycle is endless.

This invisible net of life
traps and snares unwary visitors
and the spiders of the world
devour their life blood
until they too become
the fodder of their own predators.

Like the exquisite cobweb,
life is also complex and intricate,
a miracle of hope and perseverance,
so fragile,
so vulnerable,
so abused.

But it will always be repaired.

Tourbillon
Michael Hermann

Oh, you twisting, penetrating, whirlwind of mixed emotion.

You have unhinged my mind
and caused unrelated thoughts to mingle, fuse and explode.

You have created a level of consciousness too complex
for me yet to comprehend.

First, you cast your fury into my mind, showering my brain
with life's debris

and then,
in the eye of your storm,
came a period of strange, unsettled tranquillity.

Finally, the splendour and relief of your departure,
when the dust and grime were plucked,
ejected and transported towards the next unknowing spirit.

How quickly will the remaining damage be now repaired?

Yet had it not have happened by storm,
it would have been a slow process of decay
which may never have been halted.

Uninhabitable
Michael Hermann

During dark painful nights of bewilderment,
tired, confused fears and thoughts
torment my mind.

Raw, bleeding hands of futility
tear at my unseen barriers of refuge,
to failure resigned.

An unspoken plea for a token of hope
to mend a broken, demanding spirit,
a presage so kind.

Alone, I wrestle with the anguish of thought,
perhaps anticipating the shallow escape of a dream,
a fantasy unconfined.

And how austere the bitter herb of defeat
which sours the taste buds of my life
with an emptiness unkind.

Hide and Seek
Michael Hermann

"Go and hide," my new friend said,
in Harlestone Firs, at ten at night.
So off I went – a bracken bed,
with ants as well, but out of sight.

The wood was thick, the moon was bright,
and I felt sure I'll win this game
But I soon learned that these ants bite!
and arms and legs won't be the same.

The seconds passed, one minute gone.
Then ten more – I'm getting older!
At last, I thought, 'Oh no! Hang on!
She's given me the old cold shoulder!

She's buggered off, a moonlight flit
and left you here – you're on your tod!
You've been had, you stupid git,
your new friend's a rotten sod!'

So out I came, into her view.
"So where have you been laying?
You didn't think I'd look for you.
What else do you like playing?"

Despite this, July 1981 saw my life beginning to improve!

The Three Peaks Challenge
Snowdon, 6ᵗʰ July 1981
Michael Hermann

Fierce, forbidding, third challenge of three,
how harsh, yet how kind, you have been to me.
Ben Nevis came first, Scafell the next day,
Snowdon today. Don't stand in my way!

Gale-force winds, eyes blinded by rain,
slippery rocks, a fall and then pain.
Storm clouds so black,
they mask goal and my track.

And now I am lost! A fool, what a clown!
Can't see the way up, nor a path leading down.
But on your wet slopes, so dangerous, so steep,
focussed and calm, I must try to keep.

Now will my young life be forfeited, lost?
Who will remain to measure the cost?
How foolish and stubborn and selfish of me,
 I offered you death so casually.

Thank you for turning me down.

Jobs and Careers

Singapore 1991

Moving On –
the Nomadic Lives of Service Children
Susan Hermann

Boarding school?

I looked at my older sister Annie, who was then aged thirteen. We both knew that this was not a good idea from our parents. Even at eleven years old, I thought going to boarding school was scary, bearing in mind this was back in the fifties when such schools were depicted in books as dormitory-based, disciplined establishments. In these stories, 'rich kids' were portrayed as bullies who targeted the less privileged pupils - and they were allowed to get away with it!

Annie and I did not like this idea at all, despite Mum telling us that she had really enjoyed her time growing up in a convent boarding school when her parents were abroad. Of course, my other sister Jilly, four years younger and the baby of the family, would not be going to boarding school with us as she was too young.

To give you some background to this turn of events, during World War Two, Dad was a RAF pilot trainer situated in South Africa. After the war, he was stationed eighteen miles away from our home in Shrewsbury, at RAF Shawbury, as an air traffic controller. During the 1950s, he was demobbed from the RAF and he subsequently joined the Air Ministry Constabulary which was the RAF's own security force.

We were a 'service' family and had to go wherever Dad was required to work, which at this point was proposed to be RAF Sumburgh in the Shetland Isles, hence the suggestion that Annie and I would need to attend boarding school in either Inverness or Aberdeen.

Thankfully, despite our worries, no concrete plans to move to the Northern Isles ever came to fruition, but, instead, a few months later, Dad was posted to RAF Henlow in Bedfordshire and the rest of the family followed on once accommodation had been allocated to us. This was the first of many upheavals for the family and whilst it was a big change for us girls, we were relieved that it did not require attendance at a school far away from home.

I had passed my '11 Plus,' to the surprise of my teachers and parents, and started first year at Grammar school in Shrewsbury in September 1959 and was just finding my feet when we moved to Henlow, so I started my new school there mid-term, halfway through the first school year. In the 1950s there was no national curriculum as there is today; all secondary schools followed a syllabus from one of the major traditional universities. Shrewsbury followed the Birmingham University curriculum and Bedfordshire followed that of Cambridge University. The core subjects of Maths, English and French were much the same, but History, Geography and Sciences followed each individual university's curriculum.

As a consequence of this, for most of my schoolwork I had a lot of catching-up to do. Still, I remember my time at Henlow and Stratton School, Biggleswade, with great fondness because I was there for just over two years. I had school friends there, most of whom were from 'service' families like ourselves, so every so often these friends would move away to other places in the United Kingdom or Europe with their families and, for a while, we would write to each other as 'pen-pals' - there was no social media to keep in touch like today - but eventually the letters would dry up.

Annie kept in touch with two of her friends, Elva and Irene, throughout her life and Jilly is still in touch today with her friend Buddy. As for me, well, I have always said I became a 'Billy No-mates', but this was not strictly true as I became friendly with Enid later in my teens in Whitby and was one of her bridesmaids

120

when she married. We did lose touch over the years but, thanks to Facebook, re-connected later in life.

When I was aged fourteen, we moved to Farnborough, Hampshire where I went to Aldershot High School for Girls. In this 'all female' environment, my earlier fears as an eleven-year-old in relation to boarding school attendance almost seemed to have been realised. I hated it there.

At Aldershot, there was yet another change of curriculum, this time to the London University Board, but now I had four years of catching-up to accomplish before sitting GCEs in the summer term. I passed in only three subjects. The head of the school must have felt sorry for me because she suggested to Dad that I might like to take the year again. In that same interview, I remember saying to her that there would be no point in re-taking the year as it was very likely that Dad would be posted again within the year, so I wouldn't be able to take the exams anyway! In retrospect, this was rather a harsh statement for my father to hear from his teenage daughter, but he didn't say anything to challenge it. So I left school at fifteen and started work as a junior clerk in the local branch of Lloyds Bank.

As I had predicted, three months later we moved on again to an RAF station near to the village of Tutbury, Staffordshire. At this time, Dad was seen as a bit of a 'trouble-shooter' for the constabulary so he was posted quite frequently and promoted up the ranks as a problem-solver. My sister Annie didn't come with us to Tutbury; she was eighteen and had decided to stay in Farnborough to be close to her then boyfriend. Our parents were not impressed, so relations within the family, to say the least, were a bit strained at this time.

I was able to get a transfer to the nearest Lloyds Bank branch, in Burton-on-Trent. I was not happy here; my overriding memory was that it rained all the time and there was an overpowering smell at home from the nearby Nescafé coffee factory and an even stronger odour at work from the hops from the many breweries in Burton! I found it difficult to settle at work as it was a much bigger branch and so the hierarchy was difficult to negotiate. I was the junior 'newbie' and was obviously allocated all the 'crap' tasks!

To cap it all, my parents dropped the biggest bombshell, the totally 'unexpected' news that Mum, at the age of forty one, was 'expecting' another child. It was a worrying time as Mum had to 'rest' a great deal and it was made quite plain to Jilly and I that we would now be required to 'do more around the house' to help and protect her in her fragile condition!

Then, after only nine months at Tutbury, Dad was posted to RAF Fylingdales in North Yorkshire. I left my job at the bank because, in the absence of my father who had had to report for work there, I had to take the lead role in packing all our chattels in preparation for the move. I was beginning to get rather good at this!

The day we moved to Whitby was a delight! We drove across the North York Moors on a bright summer's day, past RAF Fylingdales, with its imposing 'three golf balls' looking so out of place in the empty moorland, and then to the top of Blue Bank where we could see the sea sparkling in the distance. It looked like heaven!

We had been allocated a two-bedroom house and it was very difficult to fit all our furniture into the available space. It was at this time that I inherited the nickname 'Fred', from the Bernard Cribbins song 'Right Said Fred,' as my 'packing' role had changed to include furniture removals. Jilly and I shared the second bedroom, which had three beds side by side; there would have been no room to 'swing a cat' even if we had one. After a few weeks, we were allocated a larger house, so Dad and I again moved all the furniture, including the upright piano and boxes, to our new home in the next street.

I really enjoyed living in Whitby; I had managed to get a job working in the local employment office and walked to work on sunny mornings along the cliff road overlooking the sea. On the wet and windy mornings, when the wind came rushing over the cold North Sea, I caught the bus. To my delight, Annie had returned from Farnborough to live with us at home as she had split up from her boyfriend. We were able to make friends and to go out and enjoy some of the nightlife of Whitby and Scarborough, like normal teenagers. Annie worked at Fylingdales, as did I eventually, where I worked with my now 'long-term' friend Enid. All three of us had to catch the service bus to the base at seven thirty each morning. It was a lovely journey each day, even in the winter with the snow piled high along the moorland roadside.

In January 1966 our brother Jonathan was safely born, to great excitement from the wider family and his three big sisters. We were all thrilled to have a brother, Annie and I especially so, as the focus of our parents was on 'the boy' and, as long as we didn't wake the baby when we returned home in the early hours, we were free to enjoy our social lives! It was difficult some mornings to get up for the seven thirty a.m. bus, but we usually managed to catch it, even if we did go back to sleep on the journey to work!

Then our happy world fell apart again– Dad was posted back to Farnborough!

We were so upset that Annie and I made a stand and stated our intention to stay in either Whitby or Scarborough, get a flat together and keep our jobs and be independent. We were, after all, both over eighteen. This went down with our parents like a 'lead cowpat' and, after many heated rows and a lot of emotional blackmail and threats of being 'estranged from the family', we all reluctantly moved back to Farnborough. Whitby, though, has always remained in our hearts; Annie, Jilly and I have been drawn back there frequently over the years.

Farnborough was just the same as it was before. Annie and I were employed at the Yellow Pages offices and tried to regain some form of social life. One of the places that we regularly went to was the Camberley Jazz Club, which was a great place to see the popular live jazz bands. This is where Annie met her future husband, Dennis. As we were back in the London Board curriculum jurisdiction, I went back to evening college to re-take those elusive three GCEs I had failed in 1964. In 1968 I passed all three and was particularly pleased to pass pure maths as I had always loved the subject.

1968 also saw us moving on to reside in Warrington, Cheshire, at a combined RAF/USAAF base. Annie had stayed in Farnborough again, but this time she was happy and secure in her relationship and she and Dennis were planning their wedding. I was now drifting, working at an aluminium factory in their computer department. I liked the work but didn't like the location; the factory was close to a canal and whilst walking to work I often saw rats 'as big as cats'!

The following year, I was twenty-one and had applied for, and was successful in getting, a job as a computer operator at Heathrow Airport with BOAC, which is now British Airways. This meant leaving home! Surprisingly, this met with approval from my parents and Dad even helped me to move MY things to a bedsit in Hounslow. I was now in charge of my own destiny and would never return to live at the parental home. In today's terms, 'out means out!'

Jilly endured one more move, this time to RAF Aldergrove, Northern Ireland, before she finally left home. Mum, Dad and Jon moved three more times, first to Plaistow, London, then to Kilcreggan, Scotland and, lastly, back to Telford in Shropshire. Dad had requested a move back there in anticipation of retirement at the age of sixty.

During his posting at Telford, however, he became seriously ill and died soon afterwards from pancreatic cancer, aged just fifty-seven.

He died as he had lived: in service.

In retrospect, we sisters had made seven moves in ten years and this life had a disruptive effect on our academic education. On reflection, our young brother's school life was also totally disrupted throughout, from primary school until he left at sixteen. The frequent change of schools, different exam boards and leaving school at the earliest opportunity prevented any idea of any of us progressing to further or higher education.

For us girls, friendships became fragmented and we tended to rely on each other for companionship, although I always thought that Jilly, being the younger sister, didn't benefit from the social opportunities that Annie and I had enjoyed together. Jon, however, was largely brought up as an 'only child,' despite having three older sisters.

In conversation with Annie and Jilly in later life about our 'nomadic lives', Annie described us girls as the 'slaves in pink frocks'. Jilly said that after Annie and I had finally left home, she was deemed 'the resident babysitter and child minder' for Jon.

I have always thought that my early 'service' life made me self-reliant, independent and organised. These skills were learned from being adaptable to whatever life throws at you. I didn't make friends easily then, hence the 'Billy No-mates' badge; this was because my early experience informed me that friends would come, but then always go.

It is funny to think that as an adult in later life I was the one who settled in one place for thirty-five years, as I did not want that disruption to my own son's education. During this time, Annie emigrated to Australia, Jilly moved to Northampton from Northern Ireland and then to Eire, whilst Jon emigrated to Canada. Nowadays, I find I have many good, long-term friends and my 'Billy No-mates' badge is therefore redundant.

My husband and I recently downsized from our family home in Northamptonshire to a smaller place in Rutland. Again, in topical terminology, 'we moved on!' I am pleased to report that I can still do the 'packing-up and moving' bit effectively -- some learned skills are never lost!

'Fred', however, now leaves the heavy furniture lifting to the professionals!

Su, Anne and Jill, 1973

Su is on the left as seen by the camera, Anne is central and Jill is on the right.

On Becoming an Academic
Michael Hermann

What on earth had I let myself in for? When I had left school in 1965 I was happy never to be involved in education again. Now, thirteen years later in 1978, I found myself sitting opposite the deputy dean of the Mathematics and Management department at Nene College of Higher Education, Northampton. I had been called to a meeting and alongside me, in the deputy's office, was one of my new colleagues, John.

"John," said our boss, "the Dean would like you to look at this problem for us."

"Well," retorted John, "you can tell the dean to go fuck himself." John then promptly left the meeting.

Such was my introduction to my career in higher education!

My very first encounter with another colleague at Nene was also an eye-opener.

"Hello – I'm Mike."

"I know who you are," said Steve, as he walked past without stopping.

I had been appointed as a senior lecturer, largely because of my commercial experience. I had been part of a team developing and using computerised accounting and budgeting systems in the water industry. Senior college posts at Nene were finite in number and therefore hard to come by in those days; it is therefore possible to understand the frustration of an experienced long-serving lecturer who might otherwise have hoped to be promoted to the grade I now held.

It took me some time to prepare initial teaching materials for my lectures in accounting and finance. I was also appointed mid-term and each time I was allocated to a class I was faced with first checking how far the previous tutor had progressed with the syllabus. The Institute of Bankers accounting group was my very first test.

I walked into the classroom, self-consciously realising that everyone's eyes were upon me. I introduced myself and indicated I needed to look at someone's class notes to verify where I would need to be commencing. At the front sat an attractive young woman, lever arch file open.

I walked towards her, pointing. "That looks like a nice set," I said, instantly regretting my choice of words as an outburst of laughter ensued! My teaching career had commenced.

When I decided to enter higher education, I knew from my own early learning experiences that I wanted to be able to explain things to students simply and logically. I did not want to be a sarcastic or bullying teacher, preferring instead to take an encouraging approach to all, irrespective of ability.

In the early days of my teaching, little was thought of political correctness. I now realise that my various exercises for students, entitled, for example, 'Titus Aerosols of Far Tingwell' would today be considered quite inappropriate. I also encountered a practical problem with my hearing, especially in large lecture theatres. I would normally inform the students of my left-sided deafness, asking them to raise a hand if they needed to ask a question. The reality was that someone would shout out a question; normally I would not hear it properly and I would look up and try to work out where the student might be seated. Invariably I looked in the wrong direction, resulting in a huge amount of laughter, much to my embarrassment.

I recall in the early days of my new career marking some work for a group of mature students. One piece of work in particular was accurate and immaculately presented. I rarely felt impressed by such answers but this one was different and it was an emotional experience. The student had taken such care and attention with the detail that I felt greatly rewarded for this effort. A further benefit from this was that, at some time in the future, that student would become my wife, Su.

As my years at Nene rolled on, I became familiar with the various academic board meetings – academic bored was more appropriate in my case – and also to the assessment processes. These included examination setting, invigilation, marking and double marking of scripts and attending examination boards with 'external examiners' present. I learnt strange new terms such as 'borderline pass', 'marginal', 'compensation', 'referral' and 'terminal velocity'! Despite protestations to the contrary from my more experienced colleagues, I felt that academic standards were on a steep decline. The word 'fail', for example, became almost a dirty word and I even heard the term 'deferred pass' being used instead! How I hoped that such standards did not apply to our medical universities!

As my experience as a tutor increased, my working life became burdened with additional tasks, such as being responsible for managing a course. Bruce, a good friend of mine at Nene, once made the observation that he would 'rather be a rent boy than a course leader!' I also became knowledgeable on topics such as staff to student ratios, known as SSRs, course development and validation, student feedback, an annual teaching staff allocation of 550 hours and the hotly disputed reduction of that annual contact time, known as 'remission'. This was to allow time off teaching to undertake research, publications and administrative duties.

Towards the end of my career, Nene had achieved full 'university' status and I eventually found myself responsible for the management of the accounting and finance lecturing team. Here I was responsible for curriculum development, quality assurance and control, staff recruitment and development, and timetable allocation. This was hugely stressful as I was also expected to undertake and publish academic research and carry out teaching duties concurrently.

The performance of sections, departments or schools was also subject to an extensive review by a panel of internal academic peers and invitees from the outside world. It is a number of years since my retirement but I find I am still unable to come up with a satisfactory response to the rector's first question to me as head of accounting and finance at my own school 'review.'

"When I offer my business card to promote your accounting courses, what words should I write on the back of the card to best describe our provision?"

'We are in the front line of world class research in all aspects of my discipline,' I would have loved to say, but in reality, I didn't have a clue! I was speechless and frankly, my adjacent head of school, whispering some unintelligible form of a response frantically into my deaf ear, did little to help. Not a good start to the process!

During these latter years of greater responsibility at the university, I had become far less casual with my teaching duties. When I had first commenced, I admit, I could walk into a class not always remembering which topic I had last delivered to the group in question. I would deliver my sessions from memory, usually without notes. This, I later realised, was not good enough, especially as the institution now offered accounting tuition for the full examination schedule of two of the top accounting professional bodies.

New accounting regulations to cope with the increasing sophistication of business and financing methodologies were being developed thick and fast, so I had to learn the new materials myself. I didn't know everything, of course, and I had learned early in this career that it was best not to try to fool students with an inadequate answer to a question. 'I don't know but I will find out,' was a much more sensible response.

Now, as I reflect on my career in education, there are a number of humorous events and incidents which I recall with fondness. The first few days of every new academic year saw the arrival of the new first year students, the 'freshers.' This was a confusing time for many as they attempted to find their way through a bewildering array of introductory lecture sessions whilst grappling with the demands of perhaps living away from home, meeting new friends, locating the union bar and joining university societies.

There was a knock on my door one September morning.

"Excuse may," said a young female fresher with a distinctive Birmingham accent. "The notice says the lecture starts at noon – but can you tell me how to find room TBA?"

A colleague who had just finished his first session with a group of freshers entered our study room; he was perspiring and looking rather red-faced. He told us all that right at the front of the class had been a very attractive young blonde, sporting a loose-fitting garment. During his lecture, he said, this blouse had gradually unbuttoned from the top, right down to the waist!

"Oh, I know who that is," said the course leader. "He's the son of a local vicar!"

Once students become accustomed to university life, for some attendance at classes became optional. There were numerous excuses, often involving a family problem. I am pretty certain that some students were bereaved of the same grandparent more than once!

The termly 'feedback' from students was generally a mixed time for tutors because they could read the various, usually anonymous, comments attributable to their teaching performance. I've always felt sorry for one colleague who was deemed by one to student to have been 'fucking boring', but my favourite one-liner was one that simply read 'we come here to be teached'!

Preparation of references for students meant that each one had to be balanced; it was important to be fair to the student whilst respecting the needs of prospective employers or higher education providers. How I would have loved to have been the author of one reference penned by one of my colleagues:

'This student will spend his life pushing doors marked pull'!

My staff resource allocation role, where I would attempt to match the teaching capabilities and aspirations of a dozen or so of my academic colleagues for whom I was responsible, against the 550-hour required annual teaching commitments for each of them, was hugely challenging. Drawing up draft timetables was tricky. Workloads on courses varied –for example, some courses required the setting and marking of assessments, others did not. Some subject areas were complex, others less so.

On issue of my provisional timetables, I would sit in my office and await the inevitable visits from tutors; some would be happy with their timetables, others would complain bitterly.

"I can't teach that - it's not my area!"

"You have me down for two evenings each week and I also want Friday afternoon off."

"Why do I have to be in first thing Monday mornings?"

My colleague Ed was the course manager for our professional accounting courses.

"Who would be your preferred tutor to teach law to your accounting students?" I once asked him.

His rather puzzling response was, simply, "Notcliff."

I was puzzled. The name 'Notcliff' rang no bells with me. I then realised he was referring to the enthusiastic, clever, but not very time-disciplined member of the law staff, Cliff Dee!

One frequent source of amusement throughout my time at the university was the various interactions between the tutors. One of the more enterprising of our leaders, recognising the conflict between staff management needs and course administration, had designed a new matrix structure for resource allocation and planning purposes. Each member of staff was listed down the left side of the document, whilst the various academic courses were itemised, from left to right, across the top of the page. Each tutor was therefore answerable to a subject head but also to a number of course leaders. 'No man can have two masters' did not apply in this branch of academia. Terry, a member of the law group, appeared as a small, red circular icon in the centre of the page.

"So I'm not important any more – I'm just a red dot in this organisation!" he exclaimed at the staff briefing to explain the new methodology.

Relationships could also become very fractious. I recall one senior colleague, who was accused by another of 'bumbling incompetence'! The recipient could also 'dish it out' though, as he was once heard shouting down a corridor at another fast-retreating colleague: "You are an arrogant, pompous, jumped-up little shit!"

The target of this outburst told me later that he only took exception to the word 'little!'

I was also fortunate to enjoy a considerable amount of overseas travel in this career. This was not just with Nene, accompanying groups of business students to Europe, but also as part of a team of tutors recruited by a UK University to deliver workshops in various parts of the Far East. This experience came about following a sabbatical at Warwick University, after which, armed with a Master's degree in Business Administration, I became part of a small team from Nene which submitted a MBA course proposal to a university for validation, in the days before we were permitted to offer our own higher degrees.

Such events were always the culmination of months of preparation, which included drawing up a viable course structure and rationale and writing modules in a number of relevant disciplines. Now members of the development team found themselves anxiously entering a committee room at the university, ready to defend our proposal. We were greeted by Professor Peter, a man with a long and distinguished reputation as an academic and consultant. He had once even been part of Harold Wilson's 'Think Tank,' for goodness sake.

"Good afternoon, ladies and gentlemen. Thank you for your documentation and for coming this afternoon. May I suggest you all remove your coats – it's going to get very warm in here!"

Again, I found myself reverting to a familiar theme! What on earth had I let myself in for?   With some trepidation, we all waited for the questions to begin to flow.

"Is this MBA designed to be in breadth or in depth?"

"What makes it different from a BA in Business Studies?"

"How do you incorporate formative assessment?"

"How do you guarantee academic rigour?"

A discussion continued and by the end of that warm afternoon our course validation had been successful, so much so that the validating University later adopted and amended the model to fit its own aspirations of delivering a MBA programme, locally and also world-wide.

For me, this was the start of long and pleasant friendship and professional relationship with the said Professor Peter. I was appointed as an 'Honorary Research Associate' with the University and enjoyed considerable teaching work in the UK and, eventually, in the Far East.

As you might imagine, delivering workshops abroad would not be without its challenges and I write about my considerable misadventures in the Far East as the final contribution to this book.

You Look Wonderful Tonight
Michael Hermann

Vincent, singing beautifully in the Singapore karaoke bar, smiled and gazed towards the table where my wife and I were seated. The song, very popular at that time, was Vincent's version of Eric Clapton's tribute to his wife, Pattie. In front of us were a number of large empty jugs which earlier had contained several litres of Tiger beer. Gathered around were several of the students to whom, earlier that day, I had delivered an examination revision lecture.

My wife was enjoying Vincent's rendition and later, as we left the bar to go to our hotel, I remarked how nice it was of him to sing Eric Clapton's song to her.

"He was singing that for you," was her rather unexpected response!

How was it, though, that I was being serenaded in this manner in a Singaporean bar?

Having been appointed as an 'Honorary Research Associate' with a British university, one of my tasks was to undertake lectures on their Master of Business Administration (MBA) degree in the Far East. I was privileged during my career to undertake seven lecture tours, including to Singapore, Malaysia, Thailand and, prior to July 1997, Hong Kong. Beyond this date, the former British colony became a crossword clue – '6 Across: Chinese takeaway (4.4).'

It may have seemed kind of these Singaporean students to entertain us this evening but I was not naive enough to think that it came without a price. They were certain that their 'Professor Mike,' to use their words, had set the forthcoming examination MBA paper in Finance and that he would also mark the scripts once sat. It would therefore be in their best interests, they thought, to look after him! The students were, of course, completely wrong! 'Professor Mike' neither set the examination papers, nor was it his responsibility to assess them!

Initially, the experience of travelling to these exotic, humid locations had been an exciting novelty. The more trips I undertook, however, the less the appeal of the long and tiring flights and the inevitable jetlag afterwards. On a positive note, the trips were well organised with chauffeured cars ferrying me from airports to top-quality hotels, such as the Marina Mandarin in Singapore and the Oriental Mandarin in Hong Kong. There was normally a reasonable amount of spare time in the various locations between lecturing and travel commitments and so it was usually possible to experience some of the sights of each country.

I was only accompanied by my wife on one of these lecture tours and it was largely, but not exclusively, when I travelled alone that I managed to get myself into embarrassing situations. The following are some of my more remarkable, and sadly true, encounters.

Arriving at or departing from Changi airport, Singapore is quite an experience. It is a huge building with a large range of restaurants and 'designer' outlets. My memories of Singapore are to some extent marred by two students, Edwin and Vincent, who saw it as their duty, for reasons discussed earlier, to greet me at Changi on arrival or to bid me farewell when I departed. Many Singaporean students worked for Singapore Airlines and so a seat upgrade and an in-flight 'birthday' announcement, accompanied by a huge cake were unwelcome, embarrassing gifts that came my way whilst flying on that airline. It hadn't even been my birthday.

From time to time, I would meet up with other tutors from UK universities who had been contracted to deliver at the Far East workshops. One of these was, of course, Professor Peter, who had developed and implemented the delivery of the MBA in the Far East. This course development had been an amazing achievement and, as Peter commented on his own experience, 'it was a great privilege to be part of it.'

Quite a number of my various adventures, mishaps and misunderstandings happened in Singapore.

On one of my trips, travelling alone, I arrived there late one afternoon and after a short sleep I decided to go out for a beer or two so I could later settle for a good night's sleep. Live music is very common in Singapore and I found a bar where a group of musicians were in good voice. I sat at a table and ordered a Tiger beer. I was a bit short of Singapore dollars, with just enough for three or four beers. The music was great and very well performed –'Money for Nothing' seemed to be the most popular song at that time and the vocals in this band were supported by attractive Filipino girls. Most tables around me were occupied so I thought nothing was amiss when a young man approached my table and politely asked if he could join me. No problem. After a while, noticing he had not bought himself a drink, I offered to buy him a beer, which he accepted. I bought a couple more drinks for us later and then I realised I was out of cash!

As the evening progressed, I became aware that a dusky young woman, one of the Filipino singers, was approaching me, wielding a microphone, singing a Tina Turner song about a private dancer, performing for money. She came right up to the table and sang directly to me.

I have never enjoyed such encounters and I began to become a little concerned.

As she continued her song, I found myself squirming with embarrassment!

"Do you know these girls?" I naively asked my new drinking companion.

"I tell them you my rich important boss from England," he said.

Getting an inkling of how this might play out, I said, "Time for another drink," and I headed off at speed towards the bar, with no money in my pocket. As I did so, I spotted that my new companion was going behind the bar where the toilets were situated. At this point I did a runner and hot-footed it back to the security of my hotel room! As I relayed my sad story over the phone to my wife, she was shrieking with laughter; I could almost see her shaking her head in disbelief. She told me I should never be let out on my own!

On another visit to Singapore, having delivered an afternoon lecture, the humidity required me to take an air-conditioned taxi back to my hotel. The taxi driver peered at me through his rear-view mirror.

"You been Singapore before?"

"Yes."

"You wan woman?"

"No, thank you!"

"Oohhh – you wan man?"

"No – I'm here with my wife!" I lied.

"Oohhh – you wiy - you wiy!"

No other words were exchanged until I paid my fare at the hotel.

The Far East, unfortunately, has a reputation for the availability of 'designer' goods which are in fact illegal copies of the real thing. On one of the trips when we were in Singapore together, Peter proudly showed me his new acquisition – a very expensive looking watch. How I would like a $10 Rolex for myself, I thought.

"How do I get one like that?" I asked.

"No problem," said the knowledgeable professor, "just ask the concierge to get you a taxi and tell the driver to take you to the copy shop."

What could be easier? So the next morning I asked the concierge to get me a taxi.

"Where you go?" he asked.

"The copy shop."

"Oh, very confidential, very confidential," he said, shaking his head. "We ask my brother instead."

I refused and stood my ground; a taxi arrived and I told the driver to take me to the copy shop.

The journey took an age and eventually we stopped in a rather dingy area and the driver pointed at a nearby building. It did not look like a shop, but I went into a small room inside the house. Several people materialised from an adjacent room and I asked if they could sell me a copy watch. A tray with several 'brands' of watch was produced and I selected two 'Gucci' watches, one for myself and one for my wife. The amount of payment was agreed by haggling; I performed badly at this and I eventually capitulated and produced my credit card to settle the transaction. It was immediately snatched from me by one of the women, who then disappeared rapidly from the room.

She ran into the street and then into a nearby house. I panicked! I chased after my card! The taxi driver was also in hot pursuit, probably thinking he was losing payment for his fare. This had all the elements of a 'Brian Rix' Whitehall farce. When I located the lady with my card, I realised that the various 'businesses' in this locality were sharing the one and only payment processing machine!

When my taxi dropped me back at my hotel, the concierge opened the car door.

"How much you pay?"

I told him. He was unimpressed.

"My brother cheaper!"

Later, over a beer, Peter thought this misadventure of mine to have been hugely amusing. I must have been taken to the wrong outlet, but I would never let him catch me out like that again, would I?

When in Singapore, it would be wrong not to enjoy a 'Singapore Sling' at Raffles and also a meal at the Westin Hotel's Compass Rose revolving restaurant. Access to the Compass Rose is by means of an express lift to the seventieth floor. On the one tour when I was accompanied by my wife, we were eating there during a violent thunder storm which was accompanied by spectacular lightning, made all the more dramatic because of the panoramic views from the restaurant. I was feeling queasy and not enjoying my expensive meal. My unsympathetic wife, though, was happily tucking into her food. After paying the bill and leaving the restaurant, my discomfort was amplified considerably as the lift plummeted us to the ground floor at a speed which caused my undigested meal to move upwards in the direction from where it had only recently descended. Stepping outside from the air-conditioned hotel into Singapore's humidity did little to help.

Hong Kong proved to be yet another location where I could display my aptitude for getting into a complete mess. A landing at the Kai Tak airport, before it was closed in 1998, was always memorable as the planes had to bank sharply on descent so they could weave their way through the giant tenement blocks before reaching the runway, which jutted out into the Victoria harbour. In 1993, during one of my trips, a Boeing 747 with a cargo of expensive luxury cars slewed off the runway during a typhoon, ending up in the water!

One thing I quickly learned in Hong Kong is that taxi drivers, hotel porters, waiters and many others always expected tips. It seemed to me to be a dreadfully expensive business, especially if you were staying at the exclusive Oriental Mandarin hotel. One evening I was in the hotel bar with Peter, who had travelled with me from Singapore. After a few drinks, I urgently needed to find the toilets.

"The best one is in the corner over there." Peter pointed, but why was he grinning at me like that?

When I returned, a few minutes later, he asked for my impression of the facilities.

"I was not able to perform the necessary and had to go up to my room," I confessed. He burst out laughing.

I had found the urinals immaculate and gleaming white. But there was a small, elderly gentleman in the room. He was wearing an official hotel white jacket and was carrying a small towel over his arm. As I approached the urinal, he came to stand alongside me. Despite my urgency, I couldn't manage to pee but I still felt obliged to pretend and to find ten dollars for the tip before heading up to my room to complete my ablutions.

"Richest man in Hong King," said Peter, when he had finished laughing. He had got me twice in the same trip – Singapore and now in Hong Kong!

During my early teaching days, I had met a Malaysian student and his wife, Esther, who was from Hong Kong. On their return to the Far East, the couple had separated but I had kept in touch with Esther. My wife and I arranged to meet her, during our trip to Hong Kong. But where should we meet?

In a moment of pure inspiration, I chose the Tsim Sha Tsui station. This is a very large structure on the Hong Kong transport network, the mass transit railway or MTR. The station is situated underneath the Nathan road in Kowloon. On the appointed day, as we descended to the concourse from the road, we could see that it was huge and packed with hundreds of small, dark-haired people of oriental appearance, any one of whom could have been mistaken for Esther! If this had been London, I would have probably suggested meeting her somewhere in Trafalgar Square on New Year's Eve!

Fortunately, my wife and I were a little taller and paler than most of the others in the station and Esther was able to pick us out and greet us. She then took us to her home, a small apartment in Shatin in the New Territories and from there we strolled to a huge restaurant for a 'proper' Chinese meal. As we walked, several people pointed at us and some, but not all, smiled. To them, we were probably 'Gweilos.'   This means

'Ghosts' or 'Foreign Devils'. The younger people tended to be more relaxed but we noticed that some of the older ones, in particular, were frowning. Undoubtedly some locals were very wary of my wife and I.

The meal with Esther and some of her family, who had joined us in the restaurant at a large, circular table, was an experience to say the least! We had no idea what some of the dishes were. We tried our best to eat some of them but had to draw a line at consuming what was most certainly the head of a pigeon. We discovered later that this bird is a delicacy on the menus of Hong Kong's better restaurants and especially in the Shatin area of the New Territories!

My hotel in Kuala Lumpur, Malaysia was a tower block with superb views over the city. My room was high above the city but the best view was from the window of the fire escape staircase, accessed from the end of the corridor along which my room was situated. After unpacking my luggage, armed with my camera, I went along the corridor, opened the fire door and went into the stairwell. As I was about to take my first photo, I heard a 'thud' behind me. Turning around, I realised that the door I had just used had closed itself. There was no handle on the door; it was a one-way only system! This was a bit annoying, but I guessed there must be an exit to the hotel lobby, otherwise the fire escape would be a death trap. It was a long way down the stairs but I could at least take the lift from the lobby back up to my floor. I figured that I should be able to outwit this fire door and so I decided to return to the fire escape, this time with a pencil as part of a cunning plan. I opened the door and, once inside the stairwell, I carefully wedged my pencil into the door jamb, thus preventing it from closing.

'Click, click, click.' I took my photographs and was about to return to my room when there was yet another 'thud' from behind me, but this time it was accompanied by the clatter of a piece of my now broken pencil, landing on the tiled floor. The other piece, presumably, was outside in the corridor.

This was not the last time, though, that hotel doors would prove to be problematic for me.

I had been quite looking forward to going to Thailand and its capital Bangkok. Arrival at the airport was followed by a very long journey through slow-moving, congested traffic. My hotel here was also a very tall tower block alongside the Chao Phraya River which, disappointingly, was a murky brown colour. As usual, I was a little jet-lagged after travelling from my last lecture location and, having unpacked my luggage in my excellent room which looked over the river, I decided to stand on its balcony for a while to take in the view, before settling down in my room for a snooze before my evening meal in the hotel.

The balcony, which was many storeys high, was small with no access either up, down or to adjacent rooms. As I stood staring at the vastness of the city in front of me, a gentle wind closed the door to my room behind me. I tried to open it. I twisted the handle, attempted to pull the door towards me and then pushed it in the opposite direction. But would the door open? Clearly it was self-locking!

Panic! I was trapped. No phone and no way of telling anyone what had happened! I was going to die of exposure in a luxury Thai hotel. 'Body of man found on Bangkok hotel balcony!'

I had no idea what to do next. Perhaps I might have to wait until the evening when a housekeeper would come into my room to place a small chocolate on my pillow and to fold the toilet paper into the compulsory pointy shape! Despite my anxiety, assuming I was rescued, I wondered whether I would be brave enough to ask my wife to facilitate these little extras at home. The thought of what might happen to the chocolate soon put paid to that fleeting idea.

I then put my hand on the door handle again and, to my immense surprise and relief, the door opened into my hotel room!

Later that evening I went to the hotel restaurant for my evening meal and decided to choose something innocuous - a Thai curry soup. The first taste was delicious. Then I started to feel rather hot in the mouth, my lips and tongue became numb, my eyes started to run and I began to cough whilst my brow was sweating profusely.

"How you like your soup?" the waitress asked.

"Very nice, thank you," I gasped, and did my best to finish some of this bowl of fire.

Needless to say, I was soon in need of exploring my bathroom with its array of confusing buttons and levers. Once seated on the loo, I turned one of the knobs on the wall and music started to play. Then I pressed a lever which gave rise to a rather strange sound. Given my hearing difficulties, my single functioning ear was unable to identify the precise direction of this sound, nor its purpose. This uncertainty was quickly resolved when a jet of cold water blasted my posterior. The lever was controlling a very clever device which enabled the toilet to double as a bidet.

I spent some time working out how to operate this lever to my best advantage, but, by necessity, I spent even longer sitting on the loo.

Again, it was late in the evening, but I did not feel, or look, so wonderful tonight!

And to Close...

Court out

On the charge of 'Writing numerous paragraphs devoid of any punctuation whatsoever', the judge found the defendant, former accountant Michael Hermann, guilty on all counts. A long sentence is expected.

Poetic licence

After three earlier endorsements, David Blake has had his poetic licence disqualified by the Court of Public Opinion. No rhyme or reason was given for the judgement.

It was not justified.

Michael admitted he over-criticised David's first attempts at setting out text on the page and should have explained the issue.

And to close "And to Close"

A writing task for our readers:

ABBA - Use this rhyme pattern to create a poem about the first pop group that comes to mind.

Acknowledgements

One thing on which all the contributors to this book are agreed is the importance of checking the draft document for appearance, grammar, punctuation, consistency, style and appropriateness.

This writing team was very fortunate to have the experienced 'Mr Picky' to advise, enthuse and correct us throughout the process. A highly experienced writer and storyteller, we were very delighted when David Blake agreed to be a joint author.

Readers will, I am sure, recognise David's own contributions to this book, as he has his own distinctive and unforgettable brand of writing. He will no doubt forgive me for reminding him that his friends now expect every communication from him to be laced with the inevitable and occasionally unfathomable pun or six. I often find re-reading helps, as may you!

He was delighted to be invited to join this venture and has thanked me for the opportunity to publish some of his writing. He is also very grateful to Richard York, the organiser of Feast of Fools storytelling club, and John Mitchell and Sarah Davies of Babble of Naseby, for encouraging him to share his work in front of a captive audience.

We are also grateful to Andy Gibney, Caroline Snelling at 3P Publishing and their staff and associates, Lauren, Rachel and James for their services provided to facilitate the publication of this book.

All images used for this publication belong to the contributors.

Michael Hermann
November 2020